DISASTER BEHAVIORAL HEALTH ASSISTANCE TEAMS: A LEADER'S HANDBOOK

About the Author

John A. Call, Ph.D., J.D., ABPP is a psychologist, an attorney, and a Diplomate in Forensic Psychology of the American Board of Professional Psychology and the American Board of Forensic Psychology. Dr. Call is also a trained emergency medical technician specializing in disaster pre-hospital medical care. He interned in the United States Air Force, served in the Strategic Air Command, and is a member of the Society of Air Force Psychologists. For 20 years, Dr. Call served as the psychological consultant for the Oklahoma City Police Department. Dr. Call has also served as a Member of the Board of Directors of the Oklahoma Department of Mental Health and Substance Abuse Services, as a member of the Oklahoma Legislature's Blue Ribbon Task Force on Protection of Children from Violence in the Media, and as a consultant on disaster psychology to the Oklahoma Department of Health, the Oklahoma Department of Mental Health and Substance Abuse Services, the Oklahoma City-County Health Department, the Oklahoma Department of Homeland Security, the Memorial Institute for Prevention of Terrorism, the Oklahoma Medical Reserve Corps, and the Terrorism and Disaster Center. He is the past Coordinator of the Oklahoma Medical Reserve Corps Stress Response Team and is presently Director Emeritus of SRT, Inc., a Not-for-Profit disaster health services organization.

Dr. Call has extensive experience researching, publishing, and applying psychological principles to meet individual and community needs post-disaster and has provided training on these topics locally, nationally, and internationally. Recent awards presented to Dr. Call for his work in disaster behavioral health services include the Distinguished Contribution by a Psychologist in the Public Interest, Oklahoma Psychological Association, 2013; Award for Exceptional Service, Oklahoma Medical Reserve Corps, 2013; Certificate of Recognition, Regional Health Administrator, U.S. Surgeon General and Region VI MRC Coordinator, 2013; Certificate of Recognition, U.S. Department of Health and Human Services, 2015; Recognition Services Award, Oklahoma Medical Reserve Corps, 2015; Certificate of Appreciation, FEMA IA Branch Chief, 2015; Outstanding OKMRC Responder, Oklahoma Medical Reserve Corps, 2015; MRC Innovation Award, Medical Reserve Corps, 2019, and the Mentorship and Leadership Award, Oklahoma Medical Reserve Corps, 2023.

John A. Call

DISASTER BEHAVIORAL HEALTH ASSISTANCE TEAMS: A LEADER'S HANDBOOK

EXIMIUS LIBRI PRESS

Eximius Libri Press

Published by Eximius Libri Press, a member of the Bellum Groupe (USA, Ireland & France)
johncallauthor.com
johncall@johncallauthor.com

ISBN 978-1-7344130-1-4

Typeset by Palimpsest Productions Limited

Printed in the United States of America
First Printing 2023

Acknowledgment

I wish to thank two friends and colleagues, Beth Pauchnik, R.N., J.D., and Aubrey Washington, Ph.D., for their time and effort in reviewing and critiquing this work. Both professionals are skilled healthcare leaders with significant experience in crisis management and disaster-related medical and behavioral health services. Their honesty, suggestions, and advice helped to refine my ideas and approach throughout the creative process. This workbook is better for their contributions. The remaining errors are all mine.

By leadership we mean the art of getting someone else to do something that you want done because he wants to do it, not because your position of power can compel him to do it, or your position of authority.

~General Dwight D. Eisenhower

If you have an important point to make, don't try to be subtle or clever. Use a pile driver. Hit the point once. Then come back and hit it again. Then hit it a third time — with a tremendous whack.

~Sir Winston Churchill

Table of Contents

Disaster Behavioral Health Assistance Teams
A LEADER'S HANDBOOK

CHAPTER 1 | INTRODUCTION

For the last three decades, my primary professional focus has centered on providing behavioral health services in the immediate aftermath of disasters. One frustration I experienced early on in this career was the lack of guidance regarding developing, organizing, training, and leading disciplined teams of disaster mental health professionals. Thus, I was forced to learn to be a disaster team leader primarily through trial and error and adapting leadership principles from other analogous occupations. This handbook is designed to share with the interested disaster professional what I have learned regarding disaster behavioral health services organization and leadership, thus hopefully aiding future generations of leaders, helping them to avoid the vexations I experienced early on. Before we begin, however, I have a couple of caveats and comments.

First, one might ask, what does a psychologist from the plains of Oklahoma know about disasters, and why should we listen to him anyway? Well, regarding this issue, let me say—quite a lot. Oklahoma experiences a unique diversity of disasters ranging from tornadoes, floods, wildfires, ice storms, and terrorist bombings. In fact, Oklahoma ranks number 1 per capita in federal disaster declarations, having experienced over 220 major disasters since 1953, and ranks third in the U.S. in the total number of disasters, with only Texas and California experiencing more. Thus, quite frankly, we in Oklahoma have experienced a lot of disasters, much more than probably most of you reading this handbook. Even so, the following are my opinions only, based primarily upon my experience, knowledge, and training, and thus, of course, the reader is free to disagree with any or all of my conclusions and recommendations.

Time is precious. Thus, this handbook is designed to succinctly summarize critical operational points regarding the organization, training, and management of disaster behavioral health organizations and teams, pre-deployment, during deployment, and post-deployment. In other words, this guide focuses on leadership issues, not treatment methods. Consequently, this handbook does not provide in-depth training regarding the actual provision of disaster behavioral service techniques, such as Psychological First Aid or Skills for Psychological Recovery. That information is thoroughly offered elsewhere.

Furthermore, this guide is designed primarily for organizations that rely upon volunteers, such as the Medical Reserve Corps.[1] Thus, readers should expect multiple references to this later organization within the following pages. Nevertheless, many concepts and techniques discussed also apply to other not-for-profit and for-profit groups interested in providing similar services.

In conclusion, this handbook is divided into the following three parts.

- ☐ Part One: Organizational Structure. This section thoroughly explores the recommended structure and composition of a disaster behavioral health services organization.

- ☐ Part Two: Operational Procedure. This section explains the different action phases and management of a disaster behavioral health team's deployment.

- ☐ Part Three: Unique Tools & Techniques. This final section describes various unique and exciting disaster service tools and techniques the author has recently developed and successfully implemented.

---

[1] The Medical Reserve Corps (MRC) is a national network of more than 300,000 volunteers, organized locally to improve the health and safety of their communities. It is sponsored by the Office of the Administration of Strategic Preparedness and Response (ASPR) in the United States Department of Health and Human Services (HHS).

Part One: Organizational Structure

CHAPTER 2 | INTRODUCING THE STRESS RESPONSE TEAM

A disaster behavioral services volunteer organization, referred to here-in-after as a Stress Response Team (SRT), is a unique Unit that aims to provide needed mental health-related response services in the event of state, local, and national disasters or other catastrophic events. More specifically, SRT members perform one or more of several roles when providing disaster psychosocial assistance. These are:

☐   Stabilize or treat pre-existing and newly developed psychiatric conditions in disaster survivors;

☐   Provide "psychological first aid" to the acutely affected;

☐   Provide mental health counseling and support to frontline responders;

☐   Participate in multidisciplinary disaster health care teams, providing resources and on-the-ground training and monitoring and supporting the mental health of the team;

☐   Help assess a community's mental health needs post-disaster so that appropriate programs can be developed and put in place, and;

☐   As trained and authorized, provide spiritual care support through accompaniment, compassionate care, individual and communal prayer, and appropriate ritual in the context of varied expressions of faith, belief systems, and traditions.

In Oklahoma, the SRT is not a local/county-based MRC unit. Instead, membership is comprised of volunteers from all areas of the state. SRT membership includes licensed health care and mental health professionals, faith leaders (e.g., clergy, spiritual directors, or others certified by their faith communities), and others interested in volunteering to provide behavioral and emotional support to those affected by a disaster.

All organizations, including a SRT, need policies and procedures to achieve their mission effectively. Clear guidelines are critical in complex operational environments such as those experienced by the SRT members. More specifically, a Unit's members will experience challenging and risky situations. Therefore, they need support from well-defined policies and procedures related to such concepts as activation, disaster communications, safety, security, psychological well-being, use of ID cards and special-issue badges, and after-action reports.

Establishing and communicating policies can be challenging and time-consuming. It is an ongoing task because policies cannot be incorporated and left unmanaged. Thus, establishing procedures and later clarifying or modifying them is cyclical.

A classic problem of organizations and individuals is to wait until a problem occurs before addressing it. This "rubber band" approach cannot be tolerated today. Thus, it is essential to think ahead and be prepared.

Therefore, a primary goal of a SRT leader is to orient their Team Members, as soon as possible, concerning the key elements of their organization. To achieve this goal, the SRT Leader must educate their Team Members regarding:

☐ Organizational structure and unit composition;

☐ Team member screening and selection;

☐ Information management policies;

☐ Team member liability and risk management policies;

☐ Team member code of conduct/grounds for dismissal; and

☐ Deployment, duties, and documentation.

Finally, Medical Reserve Corps SRT members must be encouraged to integrate with their local MRC units. To aid SRT members in accomplishing this integration, their leadership should ask each to address the following questions:

☐ Does the Team Member know the name, address, and phone number of the MRC Unit Leader in the county/area where they reside, i.e., the Unit with which they are most likely to deploy?

☐ Have they introduced themselves to this individual in person or by phone?

☐ Do they know how their MRC Unit Leader and the SRT Unit Team Leader will most likely notify them of possible imminent deployment?

☐ Have they asked their MRC Unit Leader to include them in their deployment planning as appropriate?

☐ Do they know the names of other licensed health and mental health professionals and spiritual care specialists/faith leaders who have also volunteered as MRC members in their area?

☐ Have they requested a meeting with these other MRC volunteers to discuss possible deployment and training issues?

☐ Have they completed the training required for their role in SRT?

☐ Have they obtained a current MRC identification badge?

CHAPTER 3 | ORGANIZATIONAL STRUCTURE & UNIT COMPOSITION

Key SRT member roles are Team Member, Assistant Team Leader, Team Leader, District SRT Team Leader, and Coordinator. All Team Leaders should be licensed health or mental health care professionals. Assistant Team Leaders may be licensed health or mental health care professionals or ordained clergy.

At a minimum, all SRT members shall, by virtue of their training and experience, function as Team Members. Why? Because it is the Team Members who are the heart and soul of the SRT structure, and it is the Team Members' actions that will accomplish the purpose of the SRT. See Figure below.

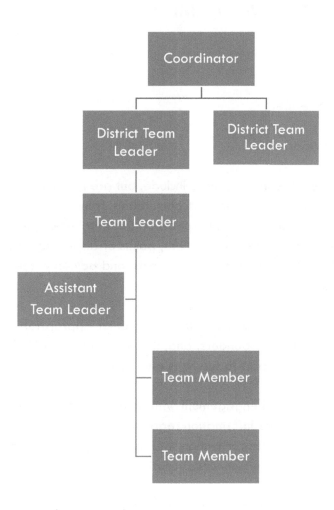

Team Members deploy in different roles based on their education, training, and experience. For example, Team Members may deploy as licensed health care professionals, licensed mental health care professionals, disaster spiritual care specialists, or community volunteers.

Whenever possible, SRT members are deployed as Teams. Preferably, a Team is comprised of a Team Leader, an Assistant Team Leader, and several Team Members. Using Incident Command System (ICS) terminology, a Team may also be designated as a Strike Team or a Task Force, depending upon its composition. Practically speaking, all deployed members of the MRC will be managed via the ICS. That is why learning the National Incident Management System (NIMS) and the ICS is essential for becoming a member of an MRC SRT.

The following are Job Action Sheets (job descriptions) for the above five SRT positions.

JOB ACTION SHEET | TEAM MEMBER

☐   Job title: Team Member

☐   Supervisor: Team Leader

☐   Supervising: Not Applicable

☐   Assignment location: Possible locations include, but are not limited to, general population shelters, service centers, community outreach teams, family reception centers, family assistance centers, respite centers, hospitals and hospital emergency rooms, emergency first aid stations, phone banks and hotlines, points of dispensing centers, public assemblies such as memorial services, preparedness events, and advisory support for long-term recovery groups.

☐   Purpose: To provide psychological first aid and other appropriate behavioral health care to survivors and frontline responders; and, if a Behavioral Health Chaplaincy Specialist, provide spiritual care support to survivors and frontline responders.

☐   Duties: Initiate contact and engagement with survivors and frontline responders, provide safety and comfort, gather information regarding current needs and concerns, provide practical assistance, provide connection with social supports, provide information on coping, and provide linkage with collaborative services.

☐   Qualifications: Health care and mental health professionals must have a current valid state professional license and be a member of the MRC. Behavioral Health Chaplaincy Specialists must be a member of the MRC. Behavioral Health Chaplaincy Specialists must also meet various other requirements, specifically those required by the U.S. Armed Forces Chaplaincy Service.

☐ Training: Meet MRC membership and training requirements plus those training requirements unique to the SRT.

☐ Time commitment: To be determined by the circumstances.

☐ Check-in/check-out duties: Must check in and check-out with the Team Leader.

JOB ACTION SHEET | ASSISTANT TEAM LEADER

☐ Job title: Assistant Team Leader

☐ Supervisor: Team Leader

☐ Supervising: Team Member

☐ Assignment location: As needed. Possible locations include but are not limited to general population shelters, service centers, community outreach teams, family reception centers, family assistance centers, respite centers, hospitals, hospital emergency rooms, emergency first aid stations, phone banks and hotlines, points of dispensing centers, public assemblies such as memorial services, preparedness events, and advisory support for long-term recovery groups.

☐ Purpose: To provide psychological first aid and other appropriate behavioral health care to survivors and frontline survivors; and, if a Behavioral Health Chaplaincy Specialist, to provide spiritual care support to survivors and frontline responders. To assist the Team Leader in coordinating and directing the Team Members' activities assigned to their Unit.

☐ Duties: Initiate contact and engagement with survivors and frontline responders, provide safety and comfort, gather information regarding current needs and concerns, provide practical assistance, provide connection with social supports, provide information on coping, and provide linkage with collaborative services. Check-in and check-out of Team Members, assist the Team Leader in coordinating and directing Team Member activities during deployment and training exercises, ensure Team Members are working within the scope of services for which they are trained and credentialed, provide the Coordinator with information regarding services provided and the activities of the Team Members during deployment and training. When deployed as part of an MRC Medical Team, assist the Team Leader report and coordinate with the Medical Team Leader.

☐ Qualifications: If applicable, health care and mental health professionals must have a current valid state professional license and be a member of the MRC. Behavioral Health Chaplaincy Specialists must be a member of the MRC. Behavioral Health Chaplaincy Specialists must also meet various other requirements, specifically those required by the U.S. Armed Forces Chaplaincy Service. Also, the Assistant Team Leader must have participated in SRT Team Leadership Training and been selected by the Coordinator to function as an Assistant Team Leader.

☐ Training: Meet MRC membership and training requirements plus those training requirements unique to the SRT.

☐ Time commitment: To be determined by the circumstances.

☐ Check-in/check-out duties: As the circumstances warrant, assist the Team Leader in check-in and check-out with the outgoing or incoming Team Leader, District SRT Team Leader, Coordinator, and the MRC supervisor responsible for MRC services provided.

JOB ACTION SHEET | TEAM LEADER

☐ Job title: Team Leader

☐ Supervisor: Coordinator, District SRT Team Leader, MRC Medical Team Leader, when deployed as a part of an MRC Medical Team

☐ Supervising: Team Member

☐ Assignment location: As needed. Possible locations include, but are not limited to, general population shelters, service centers, community outreach teams, family reception centers, family assistance centers, respite centers, hospitals and hospital emergency rooms, emergency first aid stations, phone banks, and hotlines, points of dispensing centers, public assemblies such as memorial services, preparedness events, and advisory support for long-term recovery groups.

☐ Purpose: To provide psychological first aid and other appropriate behavioral health care services to survivors and frontline survivors. If leading a Task Force Team, including a Behavioral Health Chaplaincy Specialist, also provides spiritual care support to survivors and frontline responders. Coordinate and direct the activities of the Team Members assigned to their Unit.

☐ Duties: Initiate contact and engagement with survivors and frontline responders, provide safety and comfort, gather information regarding current needs and concerns, provide practical assistance, provide connection with social supports, provide information on coping, and provide linkage with collaborative services. Check-in and check-out Team Members, coordinate and direct Team Member activities during deployment and training exercises, ensure Team Members are working within the scope of services for which they are trained and credentialed, provide the District SRT Team Leader and Coordinator with information regarding services provided and the activities of the Team during deployment and training. When deployed as part of an MRC Medical Team, assist the Team Leader report and coordinate with the Medical Team Leader.

☐ Qualifications: Have a valid professional license in a health care or mental health care profession, have met SRT Certification for Team Leader, and be a member of the MRC. Has participated in SRT Team Leadership Training and has been selected by the Coordinator to function as a Team Leader.

☐ Training: Meet MRC membership and training requirements plus those training requirements unique to the SRT.

☐ Time commitment: To be determined by the circumstances.

☐ Check-in/check-out duties: As the circumstances warrant, check in and check out with the outgoing or incoming Team Leader, District SRT Team Leader, Coordinator, and the MRC supervisor responsible for MRC services provided at the location.

JOB ACTION SHEET | DISTRICT TEAM LEADER

☐ Job title: District SRT Team Leader

☐ Supervisor: 1) SRT Unit Coordinator. 2) Medical Team Leader (physician) when deployed as a part of a Medical Team. 3) Works closely and collaboratively but is not directly supervised by the District MRC Unit Coordinator concerning the provision of Stress

Response Team services within the jurisdiction of another designated MRC unit.

☐ Supervising: Team Member and Team Leader

☐ Assignment location: As needed. Possible locations include, but are not limited to, general population shelters, service centers, community outreach teams, family reception centers, family assistance centers, respite centers, hospitals and hospital emergency rooms, emergency first aid stations, phone banks and hotlines, points of dispensing centers, public assemblies such as memorial services, preparedness events, and advisory support for long-term recovery groups.

☐ Purpose: To coordinate and direct the activities of the SRT Team Leaders and Team Members assigned to their District Unit. (Note that the District MRC Unit is not the same as the Stress Response Team Unit.) To administratively work with the local MRC district's Unit Coordinator to organize, manage, and synchronize all Stress Response Team activities before, during, and after deployments within the assigned district.

☐ Duties: Work with the local district's MRC Unit Coordinator to administratively organize, manage, and synchronize all Stress Response Team activities before, during, and after deployments within the assigned district. Check-in and check-out Team Leaders and Members, coordinate and direct Team Leaders and Member activities during deployment and training exercises, and provide both the District Unit Coordinator and the SRT Unit Coordinator with information regarding services provided and the activities of the Team Members during deployment and training. When deployed as part of an MRC Medical Team, report and coordinate with the Medical Team Leader.

☐ Qualifications: Have a valid professional license in a health or mental health care profession, have met SRT Certification for Team Leader, and be a member of the MRC. Has participated in District SRT Team Leadership Training and has been selected by the Coordinator to function as a District Team Leader.

☐ Training: Meet MRC membership and training requirements plus those training requirements unique to the SRT.

☐ Time commitment: To be determined by the circumstances.

☐ Check-in/check-out duties: As the circumstances warrant, check-in and check-out with the MRC Unit Coordinator, SRT Unit Coordinator, and MRC supervisor responsible for MRC services provided at the deployment location.

JOB ACTION SHEET | COORDINATOR

- ☐ Job title: Coordinator

- ☐ Supervisor: None; however, coordinates with State MRC Administrator

- ☐ Supervising: District SRT Team Leaders, Team Leaders, Team Members

- ☐ Assignment location: As needed. Locations may include, but are not limited to, general population shelters, service centers, community outreach teams, family reception centers, family assistance centers, respite centers, hospitals and hospital emergency rooms, emergency first aid stations, phone banks and hotlines, points of dispensing centers, public assemblies such as memorial services, preparedness events, and advisory support for long-term recovery groups.

- ☐ Purpose: To provide management and guidance for the SRT by ensuring redundancy in leadership.

- ☐ Duties: Designing, coordinating, managing, and directing all services and activities of the SRT. Managing/overseeing any financial/grant-related activities of the SRT. Verifying credentialing of SRT members. Linkage with other agencies/organizations to facilitate service and avoid redundancy. Acting as SRT representative to the state MRC Steering Committee and other local, state, and national committees as needed. Other duties as assigned by the State MRC Administrator.

- ☐ Qualifications: Have appropriate experience and training.

- ☐ Training: Meet MRC membership and training requirements plus those training requirements unique to the SRT.

- ☐ Time commitment: To be determined by the circumstances.

- ☐ Check-in/check-out duties: Not applicable unless providing services on site.

CHAPTER 4 | TEAM MEMBER SELECTION, TRAINING, AND SUPERVISION

All SRT members must complete an application for the State's MRC. SRT members must pass the required background check, be accepted as a member of the MRC, and meet the minimum training requirements specified by the State's MRC for their particular role.

Once a volunteer is a bona fide member of the MRC and has expressed an interest in joining the SRT, they become eligible to participate in SRT Training. Besides managing deployment operations, developing, supervising, and leading Team Member training is the most crucial task of SRT leadership. Training is the most critical function of SRT leadership for the following reasons:

☐ Training provides the mechanism whereby Team Members learn to both perform the duties of a disaster behavioral health service provider and to accept the authority of SRT leaders as respect and trust for the latter is earned via the tutoring process;

☐ Training provides a procedure whereby Team Members can be judged as to their character, dedication, and motivation to the mission and appropriate action taken as needed;

☐ Training provides the opportunity to identify potential leaders and then promote them to positions of responsibility and;

☐ Training provides the opportunity to develop a sense of teamwork and esprit de corps.

The training curriculum should focus on the following areas:

☐ Operational management and procedure;

☐ CPR and First Aid;

☐ Individual-oriented disaster behavioral health-related services and;

☐ Community-oriented disaster behavioral health-related services.

TRAINING CURRICULUM TOPIC 1 | OPERATIONAL MANAGEMENT & PROCEDURE

The principle training tool for this topic is an all-day PowerPoint-assisted presentation entitled "Preparing for Disaster: The Stress Response Team Playbook." This table top seminar utilizes a disaster scenario work-shop style arrangement designed to introduce and educate Team Members, and in particular potential Team Leaders, to the totality of disaster services, including pre-deployment, activation, deployment, and post-deployment execution, administrative, and command and control issues and processes. This course is a required course for all SRT leaders.[2]

TRAINING CURRICULUM TOPIC 2 | CPR AND FIRST AID

These courses are self-explanatory. Trainers and specific curricula include those associated with the American Heart Association's Heartsaver Courses and others.

TRAINING CURRICULUM TOPIC 3 | INDIVIDUAL-ORIENTED DISASTER BEHAVIORAL HEALTH-RELATED SERVICES

Course 1 | Psychological First Aid

Psychological First Aid (PFA) is an evidence-informed modular approach for assisting people in the immediate aftermath of disaster and terrorism to reduce initial distress and foster short and long-term adaptive functioning. Non-mental health experts can use it, such as responders and community volunteers. PFA comprises eight core actions. These are:

☐ Contact & Engagement;

☐ Safety & Comfort;

☐ Stabilization (if needed);

☐ Information Gathering;

☐ Practical Assistance;

---

[2] Copies of Team Member PowerPoint training presentations may be requested, for a minimal shipping and handling fee, from the author.

☐ Connection with Social Supports;

☐ Information on Coping and;

☐ Linkage with Collaborative Service.

PFA training is an all-day class required for all SRT Team Members.[3]

Course 2 | Skills for Psychological Recovery

Skills for Psychological Recovery (SPR) is a professionally administered intervention that follows Psychological First Aid. SPR aims to help survivors acquire skills to manage distress and cope with post-disaster stress and adversity. SPR comprises six core actions. These are:

☐ Gathering Information & Prioritizing Assistance;

☐ Building Problem-Solving Skills;

☐ Promoting Positive Activities;

☐ Managing Reactions;

☐ Promoting Helpful Thinking and;

☐ Rebuilding Healthy Social Connections.

SPR was developed jointly by the National Center for PTSD and the National Child Traumatic Stress Network. This all-day course is provided to all licensed health care and mental health care professionals who are members of SRT.[4]

---

[3] The Psychological First Aid Field Operations Guide: 2nd Edition can be obtained at this internet address at no cost—www.nctsn.org.

[4] The Skills for Psychological Recovery: Field Operations Guide can be obtained at this internet address at no cost—www.ptsd.va.gov.

Course 3 | Trauma Scene Medical & Psychological First Aid: Skills for the Initial Trauma Scene Responder

Trauma Scene Medical and Psychological First Aid is a half-day course designed to prepare Team Members with the basic emergency medical skills (e.g., tourniquet use, chest seal applications, etc.) needed to immediately respond to a mass trauma disaster until professional first responders arrive. This course introduces and trains volunteers in the practical framework required for prioritized trauma care utilizing the mnemonic RAPID MARCH. The mnemonic RAPID (Rapport, Assessment, Prioritization, Intervention, Disposition) represents an abbreviated Psychological First Aid specially designed for use when addressing MARCH (Massive Hemorrhage, Airway Control, Respiratory Support, Circulation, Hypothermia, Head Injury) trauma issues simultaneously on scene. This course was designed and copyrighted by the author and Kathryn Wickham, MS, RN, CPN.

Course 4 | Reboot & Providing CAARE

Reboot & Providing CAARE is a half-day course explicitly designed to provide disaster volunteers with the tools to cope with the effects and after-effects of trauma they may experience or have experienced due to their disaster service and help "reboot" and ready themselves for future deployments. This course was designed and copyrighted by the author. Part 3: Unique Tools & Techniques provides more detail regarding this training.

TRAINING CURRICULUM TOPIC 4 | COMMUNITY-ORIENTED DISASTER BEHAVIORAL HEALTH-RELATED SERVICES

Course 1 | Introduction to the Community Resilience Recovery Tool

This one-day course teaches select Team Members the application of the Community Resilience Recovery Tool—a unique technique designed to assist a community, rather than an individual, to adjust to experiencing a disaster.

The author has observed that all, or almost all, disaster behavioral health-related services are designed principally for application to individual disaster survivors. Stress Response Teams travel to a disaster site and provide such services as psychological first aid or skills for psychological recovery. Although this is an appropriate disaster aid application, it is not enough. By focusing only on the individual survivor, one is not addressing the impact of the disaster on the community as a whole. The community is also a survivor.

Thus, the author developed a disaster behavioral health tool, the Community Resilience Recovery Tool (CRRT), explicitly designed to help communities in the aftermath of a disaster. More specifically, the CRRT reduces a community's emotional and spiritual distress caused by traumatic events and fosters short and long-term adaptive functioning. Select SRT Team Members are trained in this technique, and when appropriate, the SRT initiates and manages Community Resilience Recovery Projects. Part 3: Unique Tools & Techniques provides more detail regarding this tool.

TEAM MEMBER MANAGEMENT

Being a volunteer leader takes more time and effort than being a regular volunteer. Successful volunteer management depends on supplying capable leadership. Capable leadership means providing relevant training, proper supervision, and meaningful recognition. However, even though an MRC volunteer has undergone a background check, is a licensed health care or mental health care professional, is currently employed as one, has participated in numerous disaster service training courses, and willingly volunteered for deployment, they still might not be appropriate for team membership. Possible reasons vary but can usually be categorized as stemming from problems arising in one of the following three areas:

☐ Poor supervision or leadership;

☐ Lack of volunteer engagement or;

☐ Negative personality traits (e.g., insensitivity, negativity, narcissism)

In some situations, specific managerial strategies may be able to correct problem behaviors. Strategies to consider are:

☐ Poor supervision or leadership-
- o Proactively check in with volunteers to address potential issues early;
- o Provide frequent feedback to volunteers regarding their performance;
- o Be open to feedback from volunteers regarding your performance as a leader;
- o Document all of the above interactions with volunteers to track the discussion and;
- o Require Team Leaders and District Team Leaders to complete a Team Member Evaluation Form after each deployment. (See the Team Member Evaluation Form in the following section).

☐ Lack of volunteer engagement-
- o Understand the volunteers' strengths and weaknesses to ensure assigning

appropriate tasks;
- o Ask the volunteer for guidance or preferences regarding assigned tasks and;
- o Develop and keep a personnel file on each volunteer who deploys. (See the Team Member Evaluation Form in the following section).

☐ Negative personality traits-
- o Recognize and inform the volunteer of their poor performance or negative attitude or action;
- o Encourage the volunteer to consider the consequences of their actions and;
- o Document all of the above interactions.

Despite using strategies to manage and address problem behaviors, there are situations where the best thing for the team is to terminate the relationship with a volunteer. Each circumstance is different, as there are numerous volunteer relationships. For example, one solution may be as simple as not inviting or accepting the problematic volunteer for subsequent deployment.

However, a more formal approach may be necessary, depending on the circumstances. This is a difficult decision and a difficult thing to do as a leader of volunteers. Nevertheless, when it must be done, it should be done. The following are recommended procedures in such situations:

☐ Document everything, including prior warnings, notices, actions, etc.;

☐ If possible, meet face-to-face accompanied by other leaders rather than one-to-one;

☐ Specifically, enumerate the reasons for termination;

☐ Provide a formal letter of termination, particularly if the volunteer needs to return organizational property;

☐ Do not debate or argue with the volunteer; instead, listen attentively;

☐ Assess and make a note of how the volunteer is accepting, emotionally, the termination and;

☐ Make a good faith attempt to provide the volunteer with suggestions for other opportunities that may suit their interests or skills.

Team Member Evaluation Form

General Instructions: Reviewers should focus on behaviors and results rather than motivations or intentions. Reviewers should limit their comments to objective facts and avoid personal feelings. Reviewers should be aware of their personal biases. Leadership should be mindful of one's tendency to praise Team Members one has a personal relationship with versus being less forgiving of a Team Member whose personality or demeanor is very different than one's own.

Team Member Name:
Job Title:
Reviewer Name:
Review Period:
Date:

Rating Scale:
1 = Unsatisfactory
2 = Satisfactory
3 = Outstanding

Work Quality: Rating—
    Explanation:

Ability to meet deadlines, adhere to schedules, and keep appointments: Rating—
    Explanation:

Technical, Organizational, and Presentation skills: Rating --
    Explanation:

Attitude and Teamwork: Rating—
    Explanation:

Reliability and Honesty: Rating—
     Explanation:

Overall Rating: ___/15
Should this Team Member be retained? Why or why not?

CHAPTER 5 | TEAM MEMBER LIABILITY & RISK MANAGEMENT POLICIES

Do all professional ethical rules, guidelines, and laws that regulate the usual practice of the mental health professions apply to the provision of acute disaster mental health services? Though it may surprise some, the short answer to this query is yes.

First, no mental health profession explicitly exempts its members from their ethical or legal obligations when performing professional services just because the services are provided during the acute phase of a disaster (see, e.g., National Association of Social Workers, 2021; American Psychiatric Association, 2009; American Counseling Association, 2014). The American Psychological Association (2017) states in the Disaster Response Network (DRN) Member Guidelines, "[p]sychologists [when providing disaster-related services] must at all times adhere to the Ethical Principles of Psychologists and state law."

Second, no state mental health profession's regulatory board explicitly exempts its licensees from their ethical or legal obligations when performing professional services just because they are provided during a disaster's acute phase.

Finally, no case law has been uncovered which indicates a civil court has ever held a different standard of care exists when a mental health professional provides services during the acute aftermath of a disaster instead of any other situation or time.

Oklahoma law does provide SRT members immunity from civil suit for simple negligence if the professional is deployed under an Oklahoma Medical Reserve Corps (OKMRC)-sanctioned activity. The deployment must take place according to established OKMRC guidelines. (Other states have analogous laws. SRT leaders should research this issue for their particular State of residence.)

This law does not provide immunity for acts or omissions which constitute gross negligence or willful misconduct. Likewise, even if a volunteer's services are immune from civil liability under state statute, this does not mean unethical behavior is necessarily immune from censure by state professional licensing boards. While being disciplined by one's professional licensing board is not the same as being sued for negligence in civil court, it can result in severe consequences, including mandatory supervision, fines, or suspension or revocation of license.

How can mental health professionals safeguard against the ethical and legal consequences of disaster work? What analysis structure might they apply to understand their duties and obligations better when providing services in the chaos immediately following a disaster? The primary guide mental health professionals must look to is the code of conduct established by their state's licensing board to regulate their particular mental health profession. These codes of conduct have the force of state law. Thus, these codes of conduct set mandatory rules that must be followed and are not just aspirational.

In conclusion, all SRT members should follow state laws, rules, regulations, and evidence-based protocols concerning the scope of practice. SRT members should not attempt any intervention they have not been authorized or trained to perform.

CHAPTER 6 | TEAM MEMBER CODE OF CONDUCT/GROUNDS FOR DISMISSAL

The MRC SRT was created to provide immediate, short-term, and crisis intervention services to individuals, organizations, and communities following a traumatic event. It comprises mental health professionals whose activities are provided solely on a volunteer basis. SRT members are, therefore, not compensated for their time or services during an SRT operation.

 Most, but not all, of the SRT's activities are provided during the emergency or early response phases of a crisis or disaster and do not involve long-term services. Short-term activities may also include public assemblies such as memorial services, preparedness events, and advisory support for long-term recovery groups. Each SRT member should understand their responsibilities and what constitutes appropriate behavior during deployment.

SRT members are responsible for their conduct and maintaining their profession's highest standards. SRT members must always adhere to the ethical principles of their disciplines and state law. While SRT members participating in MRC-sanctioned activities may find themselves providing professional services in non-traditional settings, professional standards remain applicable in all those activities.

For example, professional standards regarding privacy and confidentiality are fully applicable in all SRT activities. SRT members providing services in the aftermath of disasters and traumatic events should be aware of the ethical and legal standards that may affect or limit the confidentiality or privilege their profession may attach to their volunteer services. They must conduct activities in a manner respecting known rights and privileges. SRT members must inform the recipients of their professional services of any limitations to the confidentiality of those services.

MRC volunteers must comply with Health Insurance Portability and Accountability Act (HIPAA) regulations regarding patient information. HIPAA training is provided as needed.

Referrals to oneself are NOT appropriate for volunteers serving on or supporting an SRT operation. Survivors or first responders in need of additional or long-term professional services after the close of an SRT operation should be provided a referral through other established mechanisms such as, but not limited to, 2-1-1, a system for information and referral to community services for those who need help and those who provide help, the State's Department of Mental

Health and Substance Abuse Services' Reachout Hotline (1-800-522-9054), or a local Community Mental Health Center and mental health association.

Because of the highly sensitive nature of the work involved in disaster and crisis response, any SRT member who demonstrates by action or inaction an inability or lack of desire to abide by the above-stated principles will be asked to surrender their SRT credentials and clothing items or materials which could identify them as a member of the SRT. Such persons will be reported to their respective licensure or certification body(s) as appropriate. Persons suspected of gross negligence or an intentional criminal act will be reported to the relevant licensure/certification bodies and legal authorities as appropriate.

Persons under investigation for licensure violations or criminal activity may be temporarily suspended from the SRT pending the official investigation(s) and court trial(s).

CHAPTER 7 | THE PRE & POST DEPLOYMENT QUESTIONNAIRE

> Leadership is a two-way street: loyalty up and loyalty down. Respect for one's superiors; care for one's crew. ~Rear Admiral Grace Hopper

> The day soldiers stop bringing you their problems is the day you stopped leading them. They have either lost confidence that you can help them or concluded that you do not care. Either case is a failure of leadership.
>
> ~General Colin Powell

It has been this author's experience that many governmental personnel directly responsible for interacting and deploying MRC volunteers do little or nothing to oversee their volunteers' health and safety. For example, this author remembers one senior governmental leader stating that they would not authorize the use of pre or post-deployment questionnaires with MRC volunteers simply because they did not wish to *burden* their fellow governmental subordinates responsible for leading those MRC volunteers when on deployment. In other words, it was decided that these government officials didn't have the time to consider their volunteers' health, safety, or well-being—they were just too busy! Thus, for this reason, as well as just plain common sense, it is up to the SRT leadership to ensure the use of these techniques to "care for one's crew."

THE PRE-DEPLOYMENT QUESTIONNAIRE

Providing care and support in the immediate aftermath of a disaster can be an enriching professional and personal experience. However, it can also be physically and emotionally exhausting. It cannot be denied that working at disaster sites is a stressful experience.

Sometimes, people volunteer without thoroughly considering whether or not engaging in disaster relief work is appropriate for them at the time. This is why we ask our Team Members to complete the Pre-Deployment Questionnaire before deploying.

The questionnaire is self-administered via an online questionnaire service, comprises fourteen questions, and is completed anonymously. The questions focus on the following areas:

- ☐ Physical & emotional health considerations;

- ☐ Work considerations;

- ☐ Family considerations and;

- ☐ General life considerations.

The pre-deployment questionnaire does not empirically predict deployment success or failure. Instead, it is designed to provide information relevant to gauging the risk of failure. In other words, analogous to a weatherman forecasting the risk of bad weather, the pre-deployment questionnaire guides the volunteer and the leader in crafting an estimate of the risk that the volunteer will not be successful—in other words, answering the question of whether or not the risk of failure is low, medium, or high. How is this accomplished?

The questionnaire assesses the dispositional, historical, contextual, and clinical events that trigger stress and anxiety. It is logically assumed that the more stress and trauma in a volunteer's everyday life, the higher the likelihood the volunteer may experience difficulty deploying to an additional stressful environment. The questionnaires are completed anonymously to obtain a greater number of honest responses.

How much life stress is too much stress? Again, the answer to this question has not been empirically determined; thus, one must rely upon logic and deductive reasoning. The range of possible scores is from 0 to 55. Logically, one can assume that a volunteer scoring 55 should seriously consider not deploying to a disaster since the risk of failure due to stress is high. In contrast, a volunteer with a score of 0 could deploy since the risk of failure due to becoming overly stressed is low.

What should trigger the volunteers asking themselves whether or not they are wise to deploy? Once again, using logic and deductive reasoning, it was decided that any score greater than the first quartile was that trigger. The first quartile Q_1 is 0-13. Thus, it was determined that a score of 14 or more should prompt the potential volunteer to reconsider their decision to deploy.

Finally, even though the questionnaire is anonymous, the resultant data is beneficial for managing the deployed team since it gives leadership an essential overview of their team's current life stress level.

The following is a copy of this Questionnaire:

CONFIDENTIAL PRE-DEPLOYMENT QUESTIONNAIRE
INTRODUCTION:

Providing care and support in the immediate aftermath of a disaster can be an enriching professional and personal experience that enhances satisfaction through helping others. It can also be physically and emotionally exhausting.

Sometimes, people volunteer without thoroughly considering whether or not engaging in disaster relief work is appropriate for them at the time. This is why we would like you to take a few minutes now and complete this questionnaire.

The information you provide on this questionnaire is anonymous. Suppose you find yourself answering the questions below in such a way as to lead a reasonable person to conclude that perhaps you should not deploy today. In that case, we urge you to recognize this possibility and discuss it with the Staging Liaison, your Team Leader, or your Unit Coordinator.

Remember, it is always better to be safe than sorry.

PHYSICAL AND EMOTIONAL HEALTH CONSIDERATIONS
Being physically and emotionally healthy are two crucial factors for a successful deployment. Take a moment and consider the following.

1. Have you had these conditions in the past 12 months? (Yes=1 or No=0)
___Anemia
___Asthma or allergies
___Arthritis or rheumatism
___Serious back trouble
___Chronic bronchitis
___Cancer
___Diabetes
___Heart trouble
___High blood pressure
___Kidney trouble
___Stroke
___Stomach or duodenal ulcer
___Other physical ailments
___Depression

___Anxiety

___Other psychological or substance abuse problems

2. Do you believe you are physically and emotionally healthy enough to complete this deployment? (Yes=0; I don't know=1; No=2)

___Yes

___ I don't know

___ No

___ **Total Score PHYSICAL & EMOTIONAL HEALTH CONSIDERATIONS**

WORK CONSIDERATIONS

Stressors at work can have a significant negative impact on a volunteer. Assess how taking time off for disaster deployment might affect your work life. Is your employer supportive of your involvement with the Medical Reserve Corp? Will you be given leave time, or must you take vacation time off to deploy?

How often does each of these things happen in your current job?

3. Do you have conflicts with your supervisor? (Never=0; Some of the time=1; Often=2)

___ Never

___ Some of the time

___ Often

4. Do you have conflicts with your coworkers? (Never=0; Some of the time=1; Often=2)

___ Never

___ Some of the time

___ Often

5. Is your work supervisor supportive of you leaving work to deploy to this disaster? (Yes=0; I don't know=1; No=2)

___ Yes

___ I don't know

___ No

6. Do your coworkers support you leaving work to deploy to this disaster? (Yes=0; I don't know=1; No=2)

___Yes

___ I don't know

___ No

____ Total Score **WORK CONSIDERATIONS**

FAMILY CONSIDERATIONS

Take a moment to assess your family's ability to cope with you working in a disaster setting. Is your family prepared for your absence during your deployment, which may span days or weeks? Do you have unresolved family/relationship issues that will make it challenging to focus on disaster-related responsibilities? Will your support system (extended family/friends) assume some of your responsibilities while you are away? Please consider the following.

SPOUSE/PARTNER

7. Does your spouse/partner presently disagree with you about important things? (Never=0; Some of the time=1; Often=2)

____ Never

____ Some of the time

____ Often

8. Do they presently expect too much of you?
(Never=0; Some of the time=1; Often=2)

____ Never

____ Some of the time

____ Often

9. Does your spouse or partner support you in deploying to this disaster?
(Yes=0; I don't know=1; No=2)

____ Yes

____ I don't know

____ No

CHILDREN

10. Do your children presently demonstrate significant behavioral problems?
(Never=0; Some of the time=1; Often=2)

____ Never

____ Some of the time

____ Often

11. Do your children presently demonstrate significant school problems?
(Never=0; Some of the time=1; Often=2)

____ Never

____ Some of the time
____ Often

12. Are your children supportive of you deploying to this disaster?
(Yes=0; I don't know=1; No=2)
____Yes
____ I don't know
____No

____ Total Score FAMILY CONSIDERATIONS

GENERAL LIFE CONSIDERATIONS

Disasters, by their very nature, are dangerous and stressful incidents. Before deploying, the volunteer needs to ask themself some hard questions. For example, do you believe that, today, you are capable of (a) working with individuals who are experiencing intense distress and extreme reactions, including screaming, hysterical crying, anger, or withdrawal; (b) working with individuals in non-traditional settings; (c) working in a chaotic, unpredictable environment; and (d) working with and providing support to individuals from diverse cultures, ethnic groups, developmental levels, and faith backgrounds.

When considering these questions, one factor to assess is the general life stress you have been experiencing over the last year. Study the list below. This list is not complete. However, it is designed to help you consider whether or not the accumulation of adverse life events in your recent past should preclude you from deploying.

13. Have any of these things happened to you or a loved one in the last year? (Yes=1 or No=0)
____Car burglarized
____Home burglarized
____Personally assaulted
____Automobile accident
____Did you lose your home through fire, disaster, or major catastrophe?
____Did you move to a worse home?
____Has your financial situation gotten worse?
____Did you change to a worse job?
____Were you laid off?
____Were you fired?
____Were you demoted at work?
____Have you been separated in the last year?
____Have you been divorced in the last year?

___Have you been widowed in the last year?

___Has a family member died in the last year?

___Were you or a loved one hospitalized in the last year?

___Does any member of your family have any serious medical conditions or ailments, such as cancer, heart trouble, high blood pressure, arthritis or severe shortness of breath?

14. Considering all things, do you believe you should deploy today? (Yes=0; I don't know=1; No=2)

___ Yes

___ I don't know

___ No

___ **Total Score GENERAL LIFE CONSIDERATIONS**

___**Grand Total Score (sum of questions 1 through 14)**

CONCLUSION:

After completing and scoring the questionnaire, think about your answers and scores. For example, if you did not answer Yes to Question 14 or if your Grand Total Score is 14 or more, we urge you to seek out the Staging Liaison, your Team Leader, or your Unit Coordinator, share this information with them, and discuss whether or not you should deploy today. These individuals are available for such discussions and will provide confidentiality. Remember, not everyone is available at all times to offer volunteer service. Thank you for your time

THE POST DEPLOYMENT QUESTIONNAIRE

Once again, we must acknowledge that while providing care and support in the immediate aftermath of a disaster can be an enriching professional and personal experience, it can also be physically and emotionally exhausting and stressful.

Common Stress Reactions: Disaster volunteers can experience a number of stress responses, which are considered common when working with survivors. These include:

- ☐ Increase or decrease in activity level
- ☐ Difficulties sleeping
- ☐ Substance use
- ☐ Numbing
- ☐ Irritability, anger, and frustration
- ☐ Vicarious traumatization in the form of shock, fearfulness, horror, helplessness
- ☐ Physical reactions (headaches, stomachaches, being easily startled)
- ☐ Depressive or anxiety symptoms
- ☐ Decreased social activities

Extreme Stress Reactions: Disaster volunteers may also experience more severe stress responses that warrant seeking support from a professional. These include:

- ☐ Compassion stress: helplessness, confusion, isolation
- ☐ Compassion fatigue: demoralization, alienation, resignation
- ☐ Preoccupation or compulsive re-experiencing of trauma experienced either directly or indirectly
- ☐ Attempts to over-control in professional or personal situations
- ☐ Withdrawal and isolation
- ☐ Preventing feelings by relying on substances, becoming overly preoccupied with work, or drastic changes in sleep (avoidance of sleep or not wanting to get out of bed)
- ☐ Severe difficulties in interpersonal relationships, including domestic violence
- ☐ Depression accompanied by hopelessness (which has the potential to place individuals at a higher risk for suicide)
- ☐ Unnecessary risk-taking

Disaster Volunteer Distress: Disaster workers may become distressed for many reasons, including the following:

- ☐ A personal crisis while on assignment

- [ ] Reactions to the disaster aftermath or working conditions
- [ ] Worsening of pre-existing conditions
- [ ] Conflicts with other workers
- [ ] Being informed of an emergency at home
- [ ] Exposure to the same risk factors as clients because they live in the disaster-affected area
- [ ] Problems that are the same as among the general population

The goal of a Post-Deployment Review is to assist disaster volunteers to:

- [ ] Successfully transition back to their pre-deployment lives and routines and
- [ ] Begin to incorporate their deployment experience into their lives in a meaningful way.

The Post Deployment Questionnaire is the primary tool used in the Post Deployment Review. The questionnaire is in two parts. Part A asks questions about the volunteer's deployment work environment. Answers to these questions can be helpful to unit leaders for future planning.

Part B asks questions regarding high-risk factors the volunteer may have experienced while on deployment and whether the volunteer is experiencing specific relevant stress symptoms. Part B ends by providing suggestions the volunteer may consider employing to help readjust to home life and integrate their deployment experiences. Part B is a self-assessment and psychoeducational tool; thus, the volunteer is requested to keep this material and review it later.

In conclusion, disaster volunteers should expect a readjustment period upon returning home. They may need to make personal reintegration a priority for a while. To help, volunteers should be encouraged to make every effort to:

- [ ] Seek out and give social support.
- [ ] Schedule time for a vacation or gradual reintegration into everyday life.
- [ ] Prepare for worldview changes that may not be mirrored by others in your life.
- [ ] Participate in formal help to address your response to relief work if extreme stress persists for more than two to three weeks.
- [ ] Increase leisure activities, stress management, and exercise.
- [ ] Pay extra attention to health and nutrition.
- [ ] Pay extra attention to rekindling close interpersonal relationships.
- [ ] Practice good sleep routines.
- [ ] Make time for self-reflection.
- [ ] Practice receiving from others.
- [ ] Find activities that you enjoy or that make you laugh.
- [ ] Try at times not to be in charge or the "expert."

- [ ] Increase experiences that have spiritual or philosophical meaning to you.
- [ ] Anticipate that you will experience recurring thoughts or dreams and that they will decrease over time.
- [ ] Keep a journal to get worries off your mind.
- [ ] Ask for help in parenting if you feel irritable or are having difficulties adjusting to being back at home.

Make every effort to avoid:

- [ ] Excessive use of alcohol, illicit drugs, or excessive amounts of prescription drugs.
- [ ] Making any significant life changes for at least a month.
- [ ] Negatively assessing your contribution to relief work.
- [ ] Worrying about readjusting.

A good leader cares for their volunteers just like a good captain cares for their crew. It is both poor leadership as well as short-sighted to do otherwise. Using pre and post-deployment assessment techniques, plus providing Team Members with the tools to cope with the effects and after-effects of trauma they may experience or have experienced due to their disaster service, is an essential duty of the leader. A copy of the Post-Deployment Questionnaire and a description of the Reboot and Providing CAARE training are provided in Part 3.

CHAPTER 8 | DEPLOYMENT, DUTIES, & DOCUMENTATION

As discussed earlier, SRT members are deployed as Teams whenever possible. A SRT Team is comprised of a Team Leader and several Team Members. Using Incident Command System (ICS) terminology, a Team may be designated as a Strike Team or a Task Force.

During deployment, SRT Teams may be one part of a group of MRC volunteers assigned to a particular site; however, the SRT Team's primary job is, first and foremost, to provide disaster-related psychosocial assistance to whoever (disaster survivor, citizen, first responder, MRC member) is at that location.

As noted earlier, SRT members will only be deployed as per established MRC guidelines. At times, SRT members will be deployed as part of a general medical team composed of various medical/health care professionals (including a physician) or as part of a multidisciplinary Task Force Team that may include medical professionals (but not a physician), licensed behavioral health professionals, and disaster spiritual care specialists. Designated SRT Team Leaders may lead a multidisciplinary Task Force Team. This person will be responsible for managing the multidisciplinary Task Force Team.

TEAM LEADER

In general, the leadership responsibilities of the SRT Team Leader are:

- ☐ Reports to the SRT Unit Coordinator and District SRT Team Leader,
- ☐ Receives briefing from Medical Team Leader or disaster site manager and District SRT Team Leader,
- ☐ Check-in and check-out the Team Members,
- ☐ Assign other SRT Team Members as needed,
- ☐ Determines needed supplies,
- ☐ Completes and submits the Shift Log
- ☐ Participates in planning meetings
- ☐ Coordinates with other health care and disaster professionals and other community leaders as appropriate
- ☐ Participates in post-incident analysis

DISTRICT TEAM LEADER

The District SRT Team Leader's role differs from a Team Leader's. The role of the District SRT

Team Leader was developed to better direct and coordinate SRT deployments across the state. Each District SRT Team Leader is specially selected and trained for this position. The primary functions of the District SRT Team Leader are:

☐ Work with the local district's MRC Unit Coordinator to administratively organize, manage, and synchronize all Stress Response Team activities before, during, and after deployment within the assigned district.

☐ Oversee check-in and check-out of Team Leaders and Members,

☐ Oversee, coordinate, and direct Team Leaders and Member activities during deployment and training exercises,

☐ Provide both the District Unit Coordinator and the SRT Unit Coordinator with information regarding services provided and the activities of the Team Members during deployment and training.

DOCUMENTATION

Official documentation is made on ICS Form 214 (or other official form) provided by the Medical Team Logistics Officer (LO), Team Leader, or Staging Liaison. Other important SRT management documents are:

☐ The Deployment Operations Order
☐ The Personnel Roster,
☐ The Shift Log,
☐ The Critical Incident Fact Sheet, and
☐ The After-Action Report

The SRT Team Leader or their designee is responsible for completing these documents. Although all official documentation is made on Form 214, or other generic form provided by the designated ICS Logistics Officer, it is recommended that the format of one of the above-named SRT documents be followed as appropriate.

Treatment Documentation: Much, if not most, of what an SRT member does during deployment is not treatment. But at times, an SRT member who is a licensed mental health professional may provide a professional service. Once a therapist-patient relationship is created, specific responsibilities are generated. One of these is the requirement for documentation. All mental health professions have record-keeping requirements. These requirements are legally and ethically required (see, e.g., National Association of Social Workers, 2010; American Psychiatric Association, 2009; Association of State and Provincial Psychology Boards, 2010; American Counseling Association, 2005; American Psychological Association, 2002).

As with informed consent, the ethical requirements for making and maintaining records can be quite specific (See, e.g., Association of State and Provincial Psychology Board's Code of Conduct § III (A) (7), 2010).

Therefore, SRT members who are licensed mental health professionals must be mindful of their legal and ethical requirements concerning creating, retaining, and storing records. Once a SRT mental health professional has initiated a "professional relationship" with a disaster survivor, the legal and ethical obligation for record-keeping applies.

Treatment documentation may be made on ICS Form 214 or another form designated by the Medical Team Leader. Furthermore, the SRT provides a form entitled Survivor Mental Health Service Contact Record, which may be completed or used as a format guide for documenting treatment.

If, during deployment, a treatment record is generated by an SRT member who is a licensed mental health professional, it is that professional's responsibility to ensure all such records are kept and maintained according to all relevant state and federal laws regulating their profession.

Part 2: Operational Procedure

CHAPTER 9 | SCENARIO WILDFIRE

Tuesday, 11:00 a.m. The Panhandle-Western Oklahoma

With temperatures soaring over the past week—plus a rise in winds and a significant drop in humidity levels—outdoor burning bans are in place throughout the state. Local media outlets report that fire departments and the Forest Service have responded to and contained several small brush fires in remote areas. According to the National Weather Service, the combination of dry fuels and weather conditions has drastically increased the risk of extreme fire danger, and it issues a Fire Weather Warning or Red Flag Warning. The threat of wildfire has been extended to more densely populated areas, including communities built near wildfire-prone lands.

Wednesday, at approximately 1:37 p.m.

A truck traveling on State Highway 270 heading towards Woodward slams into a utility pole after the right front tire blows out, and the driver loses control of the vehicle. While the driver's injuries are minor, the accident knocks down the utility pole. Sparks from the downed utility lines immediately ignite a small fire in the dry undergrowth. Several concerned citizens stopped to assist the driver and attempt to bring the fire under control.

Very quickly, the fire grows much more significant, and the concerned citizens abandon their attempt to control the fire and immediately call 911 for assistance. The Laverne Volunteer Fire Department arrives within 12 minutes and begins to work on controlling the wildfire. With winds gusting as high as 16 MPH, the fire is spreading quickly, and the fire department does not have the necessary equipment or workforce to bring it under control.

As the fire department radios for assistance from the State Forest Service, they decide to pull back from the fire and consolidate their operations with other local community Volunteer Fire Departments who have just arrived on the scene.

The wildfire (Identified in RED on the below map) has already consumed over 250 acres.

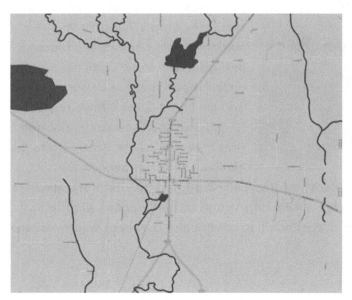

With strong winds blowing from the west, the wildfire continues its easterly path of destruction. Another couple of hours go by before a Wildfire Suppression Team (WST) from the State's Forestry Service arrives on site.

With winds out of the west now gusting up to 20 MPH, the WST's Incident Commander believes that the residents of Laverne may be in danger. He has notified the county emergency management agency to provide an update on the wildfire and informs the emergency manager that Laverne might need to be evacuated.

Thursday, 10:10 a.m.

The county emergency management agency has decided that Laverne needs to be evacuated due to the approaching wildfire.

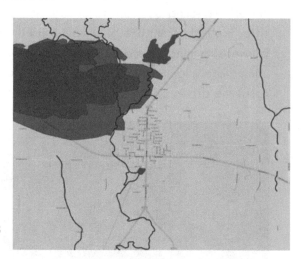

As the wildfire continues its eastward path of destruction, local law enforcement and other agencies are supporting the evacuation of Laverne, with citizens being directed to shelters in Buffalo and Fort Supply. [5]

---

[5] The wildfires will eventually destroy several hundreds of thousands of acres and force the evacuation of eleven towns, some more than once.

Thursday, 11:30 p.m. Oklahoma City

You, the Unit Coordinator of your state's MRC Stress Response Team, are contacted late at night at your home by the appropriate state authorities and requested to immediately deploy your teams to Buffalo and Fort Supply to provide disaster behavioral health services to more than twelve hundred displaced citizens for the foreseeable future. The shelters are over four hours drive from your home. Are you prepared and able to accomplish the requested mission? Yes or no?

CHAPTER 10 | PLANNING & THE FOUR PHASES OF OPERATIONS

> In preparing for battle, I have found that plans are useless, but planning is indispensable. ~General Dwight D. Eisenhower

> Plans are worthless, but planning is everything. ~Sir Winston Churchill

PHASE 1: BEFORE DEPLOYMENT-SITUATIONAL AWARENESS, PREPARATION, & COMMUNICATION

Before deployment is the time for training and preparation. Training not only in disaster behavioral service techniques but also in the unit's organizational structure and operational procedure during deployment before and after. SRT Team Members and Leadership should be taught to maintain situational awareness regarding possible developing threats, particularly concerning their locale. Once such a potential threat is recognized, SRT Team Members and Leaders should be encouraged to communicate that potential to local Team Leaders, District Team Leaders, and the Unit Coordinator. Communication can occur via formal or informal means, from telephone calls, texts, emails, or postings on select social media, such as a closed Facebook page shared by all SRT Team Members.

The provision of disaster behavioral health services is not an informal nor a self-initiated process. For example, it is inappropriate for a SRT to show up at a disaster site and begin offering professional assistance willy-nilly to passersby. A considerable number of organizations participate in providing disaster-related aid, and they demonstrate a significant level of professionalism. Most citizens do not fully recognize that, by far, the majority of goods and services supplied to survivors in the immediate aftermath of a disaster come not from local, state, or federal government but from Voluntary Organizations Active in Disaster (VOADs), such organizations include the American Red Cross, Catholic Charities, the Salvation Army and others.[6] Therefore, a significant part of the training and preparation of SRT leadership is learning who these organizations are, where they are located in one's state and locale, and who their leadership is. The principal way to accomplish this goal is to become a member (or a regular guest) of the state's VOAD and attend that organization's meetings.

In the above scenario, a northwest Oklahoma SRT District Team Leader became aware of the wildfire late Wednesday and notified the Unit Coordinator. At this point, the Unit Coordinator crafted a Warning Alert using the Operations Order five-paragraph format and posted the Warning Alert on the SRT closed Facebook page.

What is a Warning Alert and a Deployment Operations Order, and why should a SRT leader bother with such seemingly superfluous bureaucratic paperwork? The answer to these questions is as follows: Disasters result in physical and mental chaos. It is too easy for those entering a disaster setting to become overwhelmed by this chaos. Enumerating, in writing, what one plans to accomplish is one of the best methods to counteract the pull toward emotional pandemonium and allows the leader to maintain rational order for oneself and one's team.

A Deployment Operations Order is a plan format meant to assist leaders with the conduct of operations. It is composed of five paragraphs. The first paragraph introduces the Situation or the area of operations. The next section describes the Mission, which is the who, what, when, where, and why of the operation to be conducted. The third paragraph addresses Execution. This paragraph entails a concise statement of the leader's plan to accomplish the Mission. Usually, this is a series of Actions Steps, or Team Tasks enumerated chronologically. Fourth is Administration/Logistics, which itemizes required equipment and supply needs. Finally, the last paragraph addresses Command and Control. Here, the Coordinator documents the chain of command, i.e., team leaders and assistant team leaders for the various shifts, their names, relevant contact information, and professions. A Warning Alert is a document, written in an abbreviated Operations Order format, that informs SRT Team Members that a deployment may be forthcoming.

---

[6] The National Voluntary Organizations Active in Disaster (National VOAD, or NVOAD) is a coalition of the major national voluntary organizations in the United States that have made disaster-related work a priority. National VOAD member agencies provide skilled direct services along the continuum from disaster prevention and preparation to response, recovery, and mitigation. NVOAD is the only nationwide organization of VOAD members in the United States.

The following is an example of a Warning Alert.

Situation: Wildfires are reported in Harper County and threatening the city of Laverne. Laverne may have to be evacuated.

Mission: If Laverne is evacuated, the American Red Cross will probably set up family shelters in neighboring towns. If that occurs, the OKMRC Stress Response Team will likely be asked to deploy to provide Psychological First Aid.

Execution: If deployed, the SRT would prefer to field one Task Force Team per shelter. The Task Force Team would consist of one licensed health care professional, one licensed mental health care professional, one behavioral health chaplaincy specialist, and one or more SRT community volunteers. Presently, we foresee the team deploying for one shift during the day. The length of the deployment, if it occurs, is unknown at present.

Administrative/Logistics: Review your family and work situation to determine whether or not you may be available for deployment. Attached is a QR code that will direct you to the Pre-Deployment Questionnaire. Please complete this questionnaire before formal deployment notification if you believe you may be available. Remember, this is only a Warning Alert. If the SRT is formally activated and you are available to deploy, you must visit the OKMRC website and officially sign up on the Event page. Finally, check the readiness of your Go-Bag.

Command & Control: We will need Team Leaders and Assistant Team Leaders to be available to deploy. If you have questions, please contact me via telephone or email.

The Deployment Operations Order is written in a similar format but is more detailed.

PHASE 2: ACTIVATION & DEPLOYMENT

In Oklahoma, Medical Reserve Corps units do not self-deploy but are requested. When activated, the SRT Unit Coordinator utilizes formal and informal methods of notifying Team Members of the opportunity to volunteer. However, the volunteers can only formally accept deployment via the OKMRC website Event Signup Page.

It is the SRT leadership's responsibility to clearly understand who is requesting deployment, where the deployment is occurring, what assistance is being requested, and the identity of the deployment site manager or supervisor, in other words, with whom the Team Leader should make initial contact upon arrival to the deployment site.

It is also crucial that all deployed Team Members have information regarding who their teammates are, including name, profession, contact information, and responsibility before arrival at the site. Finally, it is necessary that all deploying Team Members complete the online Pre-Deployment Questionnaire and their responses analyzed by the Unit Coordinator and shared with the District Team Leader and Team Leader(s) as appropriate. More detail regarding the Pre-Deployment Questionnaire is provided in Chapter 7 of this guide.

Finally, as discussed above, the Coordinator should craft a formal Deployment Operations Order and share it with their leadership team.

PHASE 3: OPERATIONAL DUTIES & DOCUMENTATION

Upon arrival to, or departure from, the deployment site, Team Members sign in and out with the Team Leader or Assistant Team Leader. Sign-in information should include name, profession, contact information, i.e., mobile phone number, and area of responsibility. The Leader should assign two Members to work as a team unit whenever possible. The Team Leader is responsible for the initial site survey and briefing the Team as to the results of that inspection. Each Team Member should have in their possession a Deployment Notebook. This Notebook should contain the following documents:

- ☐ ICS Form 214

- ☐ Personnel Roster

- ☐ Shift Log

- ☐ Critical Incident Fact Sheets and

- ☐ Survivor Mental Health Service Contact Records

The Personnel Roster is filled out by each Team Member at the beginning of a shift and used as an individual aide-memoire. Each Team Member should complete the Critical Incident Fact Sheet and Survivor Mental Health Service Contact Record as required. The Team Member should keep the latter document for their professional records but share the information with the Team Leader. If a Critical Incident Fact Sheet is completed, that form should be shared with the Team Leader. Finally, each Team Member should complete a Shift Log at the end of their shift and provide it to the Team Leader.

Likewise, at the end of the shift, the Team Leader or Assistant Team Leader must complete a Shift Log for the entire Team, which should include a description of any Critical Incident, number of Mental Health Service Contacts documented, and share it with the Unit Coordinator (and District Team Leader as appropriate). Sharing can be accomplished in person or by other suitable methods, such as via text or emailed photos of the document.

PHASE 4: TEAM DEMOBILIZATION

Once a Team Member is no longer deployed, which may occur while the SRT remains activated, they are requested to complete an After-Action Report and the Post-Deployment Questionnaire once they return home. After deployment, the Unit Coordinator and the relevant District Team Leader(s) are responsible for reviewing all After-Action Reports and Post-Deployment Questionnaires and developing appropriate follow-up tasks as necessary. One such job should include an after-action conference in person or via tele-media, where SRT leadership can discuss relevant issues and lessons learned.

CHAPTER 11 | DEPLOYMENT OPERATION FORMS
FORM 1 | DEPLOYMENT OPERATIONS ORDER

TO:

FROM:

DATE:

RE:

SITUATION:

MISSION:

EXECUTION:

ADMINISTRATIVE/LOGISTICS:

COMMAND & CONTROL:

FORM 2 | PERSONNEL ROSTER

BACKGROUND

1.   Date/Time of Shift:

2.   Site Location:

3.   Site Manager &/or Medical Team Leader (name and cell phone number):

SRT PERSONNEL ON SHIFT

4.   SRT shift supervisor (name and cell phone number):

5.   SRT assistant shift supervisor (name and cell phone number):

6.   SRT members on shift (name(s) and cell phone number(s)):

FORM 3 | SRT SHIFT LOG

Recordkeeping during a crisis may appear to be of secondary importance. It is not. Having a record of information received, decisions made, and steps taken is essential both during and after the crisis.

☐   During a crisis, the log is a tool to share information among individuals or teams. As a crisis continues, Team Members are likely to come and go; the log provides information critical to the smooth transfer to relief staff.

☐   During the crisis, the writer must analyze what has occurred and think more clearly. Such writing and clarifying issues assist in formulating and evaluating responses to crises.

☐   After the crisis, having a log is critical in placing a given action in its context, explaining and justifying decisions. Additionally, a log is helpful for both post-incident debriefing and training.

BACKGROUND

1.   Date/Time of Shift:

2.   Site Location:

3.   SRT shift supervisor (name and cell phone number):

SHIFT LOG (describe general activities during the shift. If a critical incident occurred during the shift, document using the CRITICAL INCIDENT FACT SHEET):

FORM 4 | CRITICAL INCIDENT FACT SHEET

A critical incident is any incident where a reasonable leader would request further information; for example, in circumstances including, but not limited to, a SRT member being injured, a survivor becoming excessively disruptive, or the assigned deployment site being evacuated or significantly altered in some manner. Ultimately, shift supervisors must rely on their training and experience in determining if and when a critical incident rises to the level requiring documentation.

Date:

Person Completing Fact Sheet: Information Obtained from:

1.   What happened?

2.   Who was involved?

3.   How were they involved?

4.   Where did it happen?

5.   When did it happen?

6.   What is the prognosis, if known, for those involved?

7.   Other possible sources of information?

FORM 5 | SURVIVOR MENTAL HEALTH SERVICE CONTACT RECORD

Instructions: A Contact Record must be completed for every "service contact". A "service contact" occurs whenever a licensed disaster mental health professional identifies themself to a survivor, offers psychological help, and that offer is accepted.

Date: SRT Provider:

Survivor Name: DOB:

Location:

This session was conducted with (select all that apply):

Child   Adolescent   Adult   Family Group

1.   Informed consent process was completed (including discussion of risks, HIPAA, and confidentiality):

                         Yes   No   If no, explain,

2. Survivor's current problem(s) (select all that apply):

PHYSICAL	BEHAVIORAL	EMOTIONAL	COGNITIVE
☐ Exhaustion	☐ Hyper-vigilance	☐ Horror	☐ Trouble concentrating
☐ Pain	☐ Excessive substance &/or ETOH abuse	☐ Grief	☐ Distressing dreams
☐ Sleep difficulties	☐ Isolation	☐ Sadness	☐ Distressing thoughts or images
☐ Somatic complaints	☐ High risk behavior	☐ Anger	☐ Trouble with memory
☐ Agitation	☐ Confused, dazed, stunned	☐ Fearful	☐ Trouble coping with death of loved one
☐ Neurological problems	☐ Motor restlessness	☐ Despair, hopelessness	☐ Difficulty decision-making
☐ Trauma injury to bones &/or tissue	☐ Aggressive behavior	☐ Guilt, shame	☐ Preoccupation with death, destruction
☐ Respiratory problems	☐ Exaggerated startle response	☐ Emotionally numb	☐ Suicidal, homicidal thoughts
☐ Other,	☐ Other,	☐ Other,	☐ Other,

NOTES:

3.   Risk categories (select all that apply):

☐ Injured or physically harmed	☐ At risk of losing life during the disaster
☐ Family, friends missing or dead	☐ History of physical, emotional or substance use disability. (Circle all that apply)
☐ Displaced from home	☐ Financial concerns, lost job
☐ Witnessed community destruction	☐ Assisted with rescue or recovery
☐ Witnessed death or injury	☐ Prolonged separation from family
☐ History of past trauma	☐ Evacuated with no time to prepare
☐ Other,	☐ Other,

4.   Aid or service components provided

☐ Contact and engagement	☐ Safety and comfort
☐ Stabilization	☐ Information gathering
☐ Practical assistance	☐ Connection with social supports
☐ Information on coping	☐ Linkage with collaborative services
☐ Other services provided,	

5.   Referral:

☐ Other crisis counseling (specify)	☐ Substance abuse treatment
☐ Other disaster agency	☐ Other community services
☐ Mental health treatment	☐ Clergy
☐ Medical treatment	☐ Other,

6.   Was referral accepted by the survivor? Yes   No

NOTES:

FORM 6 | AFTER-ACTION REPORT

Deployment:

Prepared by:

Deployment Data Overview

General Data	
Dates:	
Duration	
Location	
Personnel Data	
Total SRT Volunteers	
Total Incidents	
Interagency Collaboration	
Government	
NGOs & VOADS	
Individuals	

Summary of Events

Anticipation & Response

Deployment

Stabilization & Transition

Analysis: Achievement, Lessons Learned, Problems

Notable Achievements

Key Lessons Learned

Improvement Points

Area	Problem	Cause	Recommendation

Other Comments:

Part 3:Unique Tools & Techniques

CHAPTER 12 | THE COMMUNITY RESILIENCE RECOVERY TOOL

INTRODUCTION & OVERVIEW

What is community resilience?

Community resilience is the ability of a community to withstand and recover from adversity, such as a man-made or natural disaster or a pandemic. Commentators agree that community resilience is not a unitary concept but consists of numerous and, in many instances, disparate components. One component mentioned in the literature revolves around the existence of social connectedness and social support among residents within a community. This piece includes the physical and psychological health plus the spiritual well-being of the population. This element is the Emotional and Social Community Resilience Component.

A second component discussed in the literature revolves around the community perception that individuals, families, and the community as a whole possess, to one extent or another, knowledge and skills that promote self-reliance, self-help, and crisis preparedness. For the present discussion, this second element is labeled the Disaster Management Resilience Component. The intervention tool titled Community Resilience Recovery addresses these two components of community resilience.

What is the Community Resilience Recovery Tool (CRRT)?

The Community Resilience Recovery Tool (CRRT) is a community intervention tool created to help communities in the aftermath of a disaster, terrorism, or other emergencies. More specifically, Community Resilience Recovery reduces a community's emotional and spiritual distress caused by traumatic events and fosters short and long-term adaptive functioning within that community. This goal is accomplished by enhancing the Emotional and Social Community Resilience Component and the Disaster Management Resilience Component within the targeted population.

The CRRT meets four basic standards. CRRT is:

1. Consistent with research on community resilience and risk following community trauma;
2. Applicable and practical in community settings;
3. Culturally informed and delivered in a flexible manner and;
4. Guided by ongoing community-specific research assessment tools designed to measure specific

target topics.

The CRRT does not assume that all individuals within an impacted community will develop severe mental health problems or long-term difficulties. Neither does the CRRT focus on identifying, treating, or referring those individuals who may need crisis counseling. *Instead, the CRRT's focus is to identify an impacted community's already existing local social support resources, such as faith leaders, health and behavioral health professionals, school teachers and counselors, community leaders, local first responders, and members of local VOADs, and then train those individuals in various behavioral and spiritual health tools intended to be used with community residents in times of disaster. In this manner, the CRRT enhances the overall emotional and spiritual resilience of a community in crisis.*

Who implements the CRRT?

Team Members administer the CRRT. This team is designated a Project Team. Based upon a Project Team Member's training and role, each Team Member is responsible, at least partially, for completing one or more of the CRRT's five Core Actions.

What are the Five Core Actions of the CRRT?

There are five core actions of the CRRT.

Core Action #1: Planning & Preparation. This core action entails Project Team Member selection, instruction, and all the routine steps necessary to commence analogous social service project endeavors.

Vital Project Team Member instruction areas include but are not limited to (1) training in Project management software, (2) training in contact (outreach) management software, (3) training in selected behavioral and spiritual health care tools, and (4) training in data collection and analysis. (See Core Action #3: Information Gathering).

Core Action #2: Contact & Engagement. This core action is one of the most crucial parts of CRRT. Another term for this action is "outreach." Generally, those who perform outreach should also be the ones who perform Core Action #4: Practical Skills Training.

The reason for this assertion is as follows: in significant part, when performing outreach and training, project personnel are acting as "Community Resource Mentors." Thus, they serve as models for the identified local social support resources. These local social support resources need to identify with these models to (1) aid in recruitment for the maintenance institutions (see Core Action #5: Linkage to Maintenance Institutions), thus providing a mechanism for program maintenance and sustainability and, just as importantly, (2) recruitment as community resource mentors for future similar projects. In other words, one goal of the CRRT is to perpetuate itself. Propagation is accomplished by asking the identified and trained local social support resources to perform outreach and prepare other future similar projects in other nearby communities or expand the program within their community.

Core Action #3: Information Gathering. Targeted data collection and analysis is a unique aspect of the CRRT. Targeted data collection occurs primarily during Core Actions #2 and #4.

The CRRT utilizes and relies upon two unique community resilience assessment tools designed, developed, and field-tested by the present author to help guide its efforts. These tools are the Community Emotional and Social Resilience Index (CESRI) and the Services Impact Survey (SIS).   The CESRI measures and monitors two significant components of Community Resilience: the Emotional and Social Resilience Component and the Disaster Management Resilience Component. This tool measures these components' strengths and changes within the targeted communities over time. This tool also calculates the perceived most effective avenue of social support provision within an existing community, the Impact Path Analysis. This analysis provides a methodology to decide which channel of social support provision is most commonly utilized by community members and thus has the most significant potential impact.

The Services Impact Survey assesses the level of service impact of selected and trained local social support resources. This tool measures the potential impact, influence, and effect of the Project's action upon the chosen community.

Core Action #4: Practical Skills Training. This core action consists of training the selected local social support resources in skills for emotional and spiritual recovery following a disaster.   CRRT Team Members who do this training should have actual crisis-related emotional, social, and spiritual recovery provision experience. This training is provided to the targeted community's social support and resiliency networks. It includes training options that qualify those trained for credentialing and affiliation within established crisis response organizations that provide crisis emotional and spiritual care within the targeted community.

Core Action #5: Linkage to Maintenance Institutions. This core action consists of focusing on maintenance and support. This action step is accomplished by facilitating the recruitment, during outreach and training, of the program's participants into the local Medical Reserve Corps units, local faith-sponsored spiritual care responder units, and other local VOADs.

As part of Core Action #5, it is necessary to identify and analyze the existing governmental and non-governmental provision of disaster-related social support resiliency services within the targeted community. Then, these organizations should be approached and requested to accept the newly trained local social support resources as members.

What is the desired outcome of the CRRT?

The expected goal of the CRRT is increased community resilience. This objective is accomplished by enhancing two crucial elements—the Emotional and Social Community Resilience Component and the Disaster Management Resilience Component. These two critical elements of community resilience are maximized by identifying and training existing local social support resources in disaster-impacted communities to fulfill their role better and recruiting them into existing governmental and non-governmental institutions that rely upon emotional and spiritual care resources. Using the CRRT, this objective is realized cost-effectively and efficiently and is validated by ongoing data collection and analysis.

COMMUNITY RESILIENCE RECOVERY TOOL CORE ACTIONS: AN EXAMPLE

Core Action #1: Planning and Preparation

When planning a Project, one initial question to ask and answer is: What local social support resources will be targeted--one, several, or as many as possible? A single target focus is discussed for the following discussion, and faith leaders are selected as the designated local social support resource targeted.

Questions:

1.   What are the targeted communities?
2.   What professions, skills, and training should the members of the Project Team have?
3.   What equipment, software, and facilities does the Project Team require?
4.   Will the Project Team be composed of volunteers or be reimbursed for their time?
5.   What is the leadership structure of the Project Team?

Core Action #2: Contact and Engagement

Questions:
1.   How will the targeted local social support resources be selected, contacted, and recruited to participate?
2.   Who on the Project team will be primarily responsible for contact and engagement?
3.   What outreach software platform will be utilized?

Core Action #3: Information Gathering

Questions:
1.   How, when, and to whom will the CESRI and SIS be administered?
2.   How and who will analyze the CESRI and SIS data?

Core Action #4: Practical Skills Training

Questions:
1.   What behavioral health training programs will be taught?
2.   What emotional and spiritual care curriculum will be used?
3.   What training venues will be used?

Core Action #5: Linkages to Maintenance Institutions

Questions:

1.   What crisis-oriented governmental and non-governmental organizations are available within the targeted community?
2.   Which are most appropriate to link with trained faith leaders participating in the Project?
3.   How best is it to link the two?

KEYWORD GLOSSARY:

Community resilience: the ability of a community to withstand and recover from adversity, such as a man-made or natural disaster

Emotional and social community resilience component: One part of community resilience--the physical and psychological health plus the spiritual well-being of the population

Disaster management resilience component: One part of community resilience--a community's perception that individuals, families, and the community as a whole possess knowledge and skills that promote self-reliance, self-help, and crisis preparedness

Local social support resiliency resources, sometimes Local social support resources: Those persons within a given community, because of their profession, job, or role, provide social support to community members on a regular basis. Examples in a community are faith leaders, health and behavioral health professionals, community leaders, teachers, and members of local VOADs

Community Emotional and Social Resilience Index (CESRI): an assessment tool that measures (i) local support resources' perception of their communities' emotional and social resilience, (ii) disaster management preparedness, (iii) as well as their perception of the most effective avenue of social support within their community

Emotional Social Resilience Index (ESRI): a global measure of that component of community resilience related to perceived emotional and social viability and connectedness. ESRI scores can range from 1 through 5, with a score of 1 suggesting a very low ability regarding this crucial resilience component to a score of 5 indicating a very strong ability.

Disaster Management Index (DMI): a global measure of that component of community resilience related to perceived community ability to prepare and manage disaster crises. DMI scores can range from 1 through 5, with a score of 1 suggesting a very low ability regarding this crucial resilience component to a score of 5 suggesting a very strong ability.

Impact Path Analysis (IPA): a measure of the perceived most effective avenue of social support provision within an existing community.

Services Impact Survey (SIS): a tool to assess the effectiveness of the extent to which the identified local support resource provides some level of care, support, or professional interaction with persons who are, or have been, in a crisis (disastrous) situation, as well as to assess the essential demographic characteristics of those persons.

COMMUNITY EMOTIONAL & SOCIAL RESILIENCE INDEX

Section 1: Emotional & Social Community Resilience Items

Please circle one response for each possible description of your community.

1 Strongly Disagree   2 Disagree   3 Neither Disagree Nor Agree   4 Agree   5 Strongly Agree

1. In my community, there is generally a strong sense of belonging.	1 2 3 4 5
2. People in my community generally trust and value each other.	1 2 3 4 5
3. Many people in my community participate in community groups, clubs, faith-based organizations, and other shared activities.	1 2 3 4 5
4. In my community, faith-based, cultural and ethnic groups have spaces to gather.	1 2 3 4 5
5. People in my community have a can-do mentality.	1 2 3 4 5
6. People in my community are actively involved in faith-based organizations which provide ritual, support, meaning, purpose, and hope.	1 2 3 4 5
7. In my community, services allow seniors and those with disabilities to live independently.	1 2 3 4 5
8. In my community, schools and child-care options are sufficient for families.	1 2 3 4 5
9. In my community, services are available locally (e.g. parenting programs, youth organizations, women's shelter).	1 2 3 4 5
10. Affordable counselling and other mental health services (e.g., AA) are available locally.	1 2 3 4 5
11. Primary health care (e.g., family doctors, health clinic) is available locally.	1 2 3 4 5
12. Adequate social support services are available locally to those with specific needs (e.g., children, people with disabilities, chronic health issues).	1 2 3 4 5
13. People in my community rally to help residents in need.	1 2 3 4 5
14. In my community rates of suicide are generally low.	1 2 3 4 5
15. In my community rates of drug and/or alcohol abuse are generally low.	1 2 3 4 5
16. In my community rates of crime and violence are generally low.	1 2 3 4 5
17. People in my community work together with minimal conflict as they solve community challenges.	1 2 3 4 5

Section 2: Disaster Management Items

Please circle one response for each possible description of your community.

1 Strongly Disagree   2 Disagree   3 Neither Disagree Nor Agree   4 Agree   5 Strongly Agree

18. In my community, most people are aware of current local and regional hazards and risks.	1 2 3 4 5
19. Most people are familiar with local disaster/emergency plans.	1 2 3 4 5
20. In my community, most people have emergency supplies at home, work, and in their cars.	1 2 3 4 5
21. My community actively prepares for disasters.	1 2 3 4 5
22. My community has services and programs to help people during and after disasters.	1 2 3 4 5
23. In my area, livestock/farm owners have developed comprehensive disaster plans regarding their animals and equipment.	1 2 3 4 5
24. I feel that my family and I are prepared, emotionally and spiritually, to deal with a disaster that might occur in my community.	1 2 3 4 5
25. I believe that I would be able to help others, emotionally and/or spiritually, in my community if a disaster occurred.	1 2 3 4 5

Section 3: Disaster Experience Items

Please answer the following questions about your disaster involvement and experience.

26. Have you experienced a disaster or catastrophe? (If you have personally been involved in more than one disaster, focus on the one that has had the greatest personal effect on you.)

    __No   __Yes, a natural disaster   __Yes, a man-made disaster

27. Have you ever responded to a disaster or catastrophe? (If you have responded to more than one catastrophe, focus on the most recent.)

    __No   __Yes, as a volunteer responder   __Yes, as a professional responder

    __Yes, other (please specify):

28. Have you ever experienced a personal catastrophe, crisis, or tragedy while living in your community?   __No   __Yes

    (Consider this definition of personal catastrophe or crisis: *sudden calamitous event bringing intense instability, damage, or danger, especially one with the distinct possibility of a highly undesirable outcome. Examples range from either you or a loved one being a victim of crime, suffering a house fire, experiencing a sudden serious illness or accident, a tornado, or a wildfire.*) **If yes, continue to question 29. If no, go to question 30.**

29. Please think of the most significant personal catastrophe, crisis, or tragedy you have experienced while living in this community. From whom did you obtain aid? (Check all that apply.)

    __no one __family member   __friends   __someone else from the community

    __faith-based organization   __a local agency or organization   __co-workers

    __other (please specify):

30. If, in the future, you did experience a significant personal catastrophe, crisis, or tragedy, to whom would you most likely turn to for assistance? **(Check only one response.)**

    __civic club   __faith-based organization __family member   __friends   __school

    __co-workers   __other (please specify):

Section 4: Demographics

Please answer the following questions.

1. The community I live in is:

2. How long have you lived in this community?

3.   My profession/job is:

4.   What is your sex? __Male   __Female

5.   What is your age?

6.   What is your current marital status?

   __Married   __Separated   __Divorced   __Widowed

   __Never Married   Other (please specify):

7. What is your race or ethnic identity? Check the one that you believe best applies:

         __American Indian/Alaska Native

         __Asian American

         __Black/African American/Afro-Caribbean

         __Hispanic/Latino

         __Native Hawaiian/Other Pacific Islander

         __White/Caucasian, not of Hispanic Origin

SERVICES IMPACT SURVEY

Copyright © 2018 J.Call

We are interested in the types of services you provide, whether or not you work with people in crisis because of a disaster, and who those people might be. Please respond to the following three questions. Thank you.

How would you describe your primary service/work setting?

___Faith based

___Medical/health care

___Behavioral health care

___Emergency management

___School

___Government

___First responder

___Other, Please specify

In your role, as described in Question 1, approximately how many hours per month do you provide some level of care, support, or professional interaction with persons who are, or have been, in a crisis (disastrous) situation within the previous 30 days? (*Consider this definition of crisis: a sudden calamitous event bringing intense instability, damage, or danger, especially one with the distinct possibility of a highly undesirable outcome. Examples range from the person or a loved one of the person being a victim of crime, suffering a house fire, experiencing a sudden severe illness or accident, a tornado, or a wildfire.*)

___+160 hours   ___160-80 hours   ___79-40 hours

___39-20 hours   ___19-8 hours   ___7-1 hours   ___0 hours

Considering your answers to Questions 1 and 2 above, to what percentage have you provided some level of care, support, or professional interaction with persons who are--

___Children   ___Adults   ___Seniors

(The total must equal 100%)

SAMPLE PROJECT DATA DEMONSTRATING THE SIGNIFICANT IMPACT OF THE CRRT

It may be difficult for the initial reader to grasp the significance and power of the CRRT. Thus, actual results from one Project are presented below. This Project was initiated following a large outbreak of wildfires in 2017-2018 in western Oklahoma and was completed over twelve months, ending in the latter part of 2019.

Outcome One | Measured the number of persons trained, the trainees' evaluation of the training, and trainees' self-reports regarding disaster-related stress at the time of training.

Three hundred twenty pre-identified and specially selected local social support resources were trained. Figure 1 displays the different professions of these individuals. Forty-five percent of those trained were faith leaders, 24% were health care or behavioral health care professionals, and 18% were educators. In summary, the local social support resources that were selected and trained included nurses, nursing students, EMTs, school teachers and counselors, licensed counselors, social workers, firefighters, law enforcement, clergy, local VOAD members, local disaster professionals, and local city/county government officials.

Data from the Community Emotional and Social Resilience Index (CESRI) suggested that community members relied more upon their faith leaders than their local health and behavioral health professionals for emotional and spiritual support in crisis. See below.

Q30: If you answered NO to Question 26, what is the source of your greatest connection to your community, the connection you would most likely turn to in a time of need for assistance? (Check only one response.)

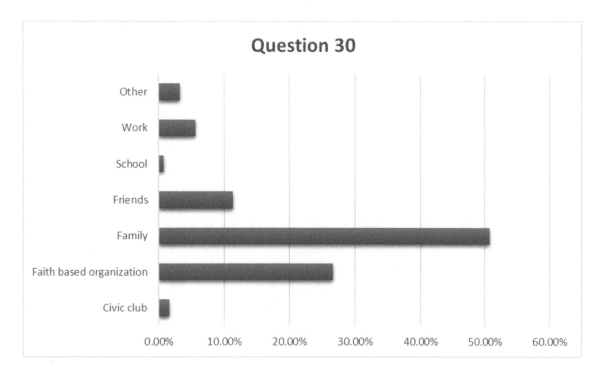

Q29: If you answered YES to Question 26, please think of the most significant emergency or crisis you have experienced while living in this community. Who helped you? (check all that apply.)

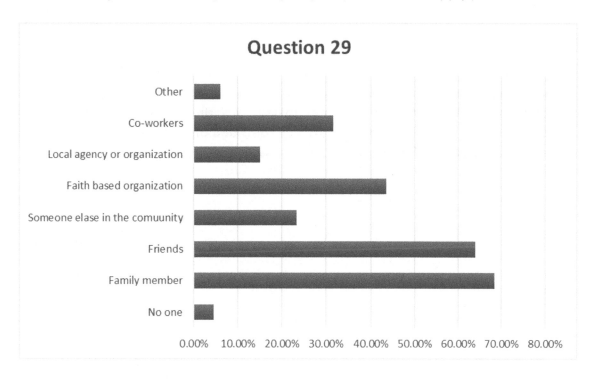

Thus, as the Project progressed greater effort was made to identify and engage these individuals.

The training curriculum focused on professional social support/behavioral crisis techniques. Most trainings were intensive, i.e., taking an entire day. The curriculum included Psychological First Aid (which in relevant instances included instruction in Disaster Spiritual Care)[7], Skills for Psychological Recovery, Intermediate Disaster Spiritual Care, QPR (Question, Persuade, Refer) Suicide Prevention, Stress First Aid for Firefighters, and a Disaster Table Top All Day Exercise. See Figure 2.

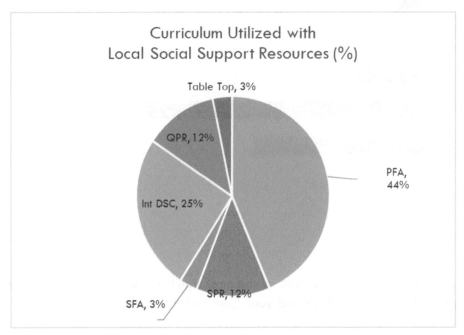

Figure 2

Locations for the trainings were selected primarily based on geographic area disaster impact and centrality of communication in the rather desolate area upon which the Project focused. Thus, the city of Woodward, in Woodward County, was where most individuals were trained. Nevertheless, a total of eight impacted towns were visited. See Figure 3. However, some trainings were provided at state-wide conferences, which, in part, were attended by members of the impacted communities.

---

[7] See e.g.. Brymer, M. et al and NCTSN PFA Community Religious Professionals Committee (2006). Psychological First Aid Field Operations Guide for Community Religious Professionals. National Child Traumatic Stress Network & National Center for PTSD.

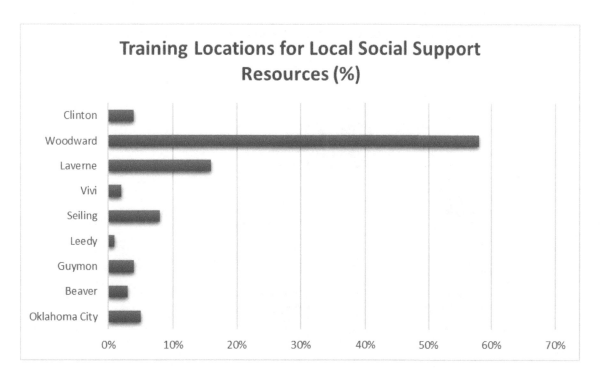

Figure 3

Seventy-eight trained individuals reported being involved in a disaster within the last 24 to 48 months. Ten percent reported suffering a significant physical injury due to this disaster. Other important self-reported information is noted in the following table graphs.

QUESTION: Did you...	YES
Feel or express extreme panic	43%
Feel that your life was in danger	29%
See or hear the death or serious injury of another	49%
Experienced a confirmed exposure or contamination to a harmful agent	9%
Undergo decontamination	18%

Felt very upset when something reminds you of a stressful event experienced during this disaster?

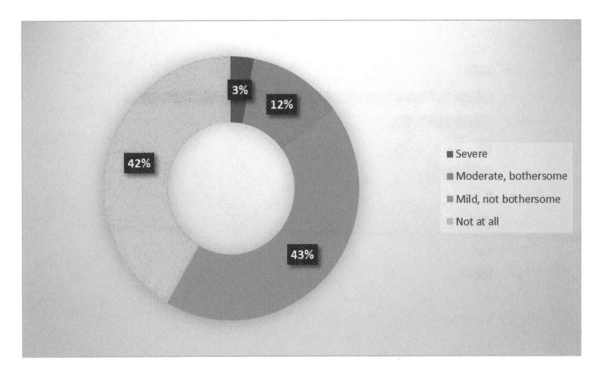

Experienced physical reactions (e.g. heart pounding, trouble breathing, or sweating) when some reminds you of a stressful event experienced during his disaster?

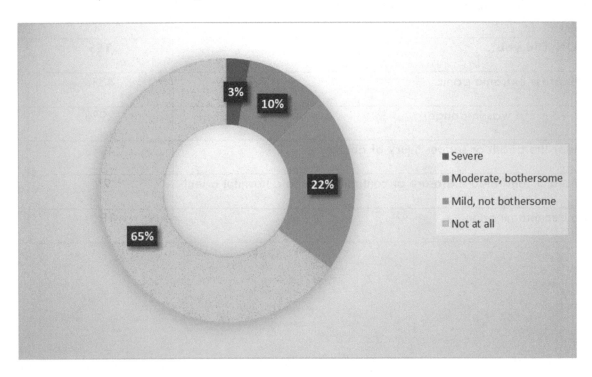

The training participants were overwhelmingly positive in their analysis of their training experience. See Figure 4.

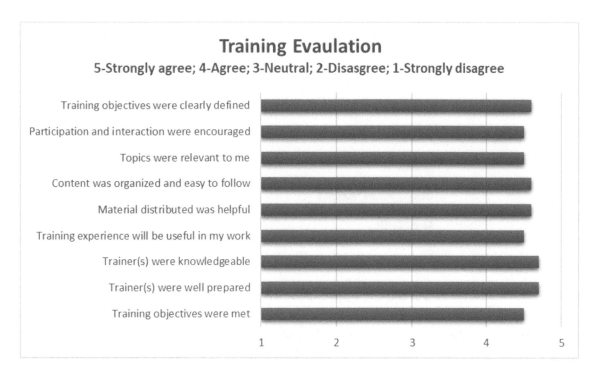

Figure 4

Outcome Two | Measured Role and Impact of Trained Local Social Support Resources

In summary, results of the Services Impact Survey indicate that the majority of the local social support resources who were administered the SIS and were trained--worked in the health care field (32.56%), followed by clergy (16.28%) and educators (15.50%).   See below.

In that role, over a quarter (27.13%) reported working with disaster/crisis-impacted individuals 80 or more hours within the last 30 days. Furthermore, another quarter (25.58%) reported working with disaster/crisis-impacted individuals 20 to 79 hours within the previous 30 days. Note that an average work month includes approximately 160 hours. *Thus, the data indicates that more than half of those trained reported providing social support to disaster/crisis-impacted individuals in their community 20 or more hours a month.* See below.

Q1: How would you describe your primary service/work setting?

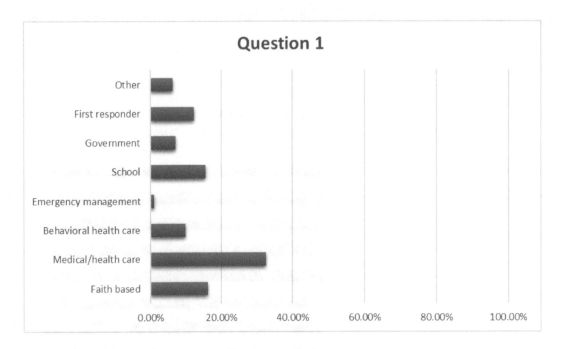

Q2: In your role, as described in Question 1, approximately how many hours per month do you provide some level of care, support, or professional interaction with persons who are, or have been, in a crisis (disastrous) situation within the previous 30 days? (Consider this definition of crisis: a sudden calamitous event bringing intense instability, damage, or danger, especially one with the distinct possibility of a highly undesirable outcome. Examples range from the person or loved one of the person being a victim of crime, suffering a house fire, experiencing a sudden severe illness or accident, a tornado, or a wildfire.)

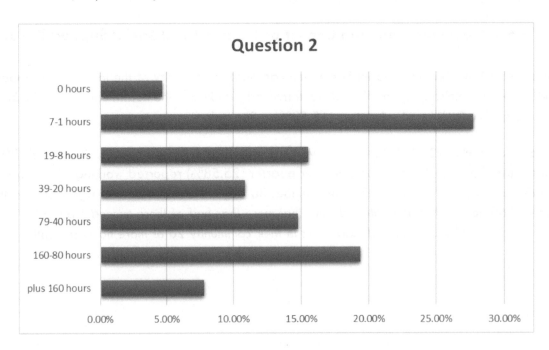

Research indicates that the young and the elderly are more at risk of a crisis experience as compared to middle aged adults. *Data from the Services Impact Survey suggest that the local social support resources trained worked with all three age groups.* See below.

Q3: Considering your answers to Questions 1 and 2 above, to what percentage have you provided some level of care, support or professional interaction with persons who are--

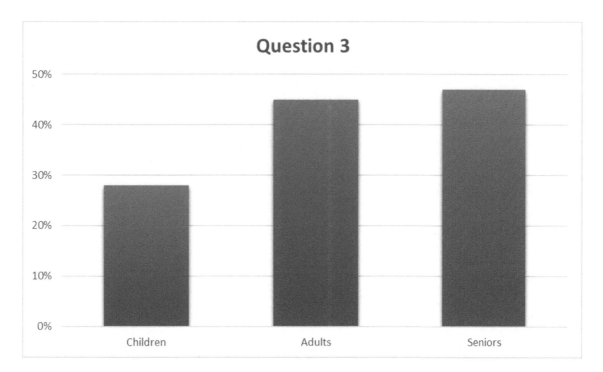

In conclusion, the data strongly supports the conclusion that those trained are individuals who provide significant levels of emotional, behavioral, and spiritual support to their local community and believe that the training they received was worthwhile and that they would use it in their work.

The SRT PsyShelter Mental Health Triage System was designed to quickly provide a mechanism whereby SRT Community Volunteers, who are not health or behavioral health care professionals, can quickly determine whether or not to refer a survivor to a Team Member who is a licensed professional. Likewise, when appropriate and with proper prior instruction, this tool is shared with partner disaster service team members with whom the SRT is deploying.

SRT PsyShelter ™ Mental Health Triage System

	Y or N
EXPRESSES THOUGHT OR INTENT TO HARM SELF/OTHERS?	
EXPRESSES SEVERE PANIC OR ANXIETY?	
EXPRESSES SEVERE DEPRESSION OR SADNESS?	
COMPLAINS OF UNUSUAL THOUGHTS?	
COMPLAINS OF UNUSUAL BODY SENSATIONS?	
HAS PROBLEMS WITH CONCENTRATION/THINKING CLEARLY?	
NOT COPING WELL WITH RESPECT TO THE CURRENT DISASTER?	
IS WORRIED ABOUT COPING WITH THE CURRENT CRISIS?	
NO TRIAGE FACTORS IDENTIFIED?	

1. Hello, I have some questions I would like to ask you, Okay?
2. How are you feeling today?
3. How would you describe your mood?
4. Have you recently felt panicky, overly anxious or depressed?
5. Are you bothered by any unusual thoughts or body sensations?
6. Have you recently had any problems with your concentration or being able to think clearly?

7. How do you feel you are coping with respect to the current disaster?
8. Have you recently had any thoughts or intent to harm yourself or others?
9. Do you have any worries or concerns about coping with the current crisis?

Depending upon the citizen's responses to Questions 1-9, see Decision Algorithm below, the Disaster Worker asks-

Decision Algorithm

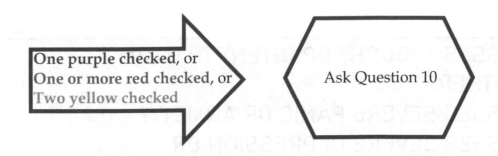

One purple checked, or
One or more red checked, or
Two yellow checked

Ask Question 10

10. Would you like to speak briefly to a member of our Stress Response Team?

POST DEPLOYMENT QUESTIONANIRE

PART A

INSTRUCTIONS: Please complete Part A. If this deployment involved a disaster, then also complete Part B.

SECTION I. QUESTIONS ABOUT YOUR WORK ENVIRONMENT DURING DEPLOYMENT

1.   I felt comfortable in my assigned role.

   ☐ 1 Strongly Disagree   ☐ 2 Disagree   ☐ 3 Undecided   ☐ 4 Agree   ☐ 5 Strongly Agree

2.   I was comfortable in my workspace environment.

   ☐ 1 Strongly Disagree   ☐ 2 Disagree   ☐ 3 Undecided   ☐ 4 Agree   ☐ 5 Strongly Agree

3.   I had all the resources necessary to perform my specific task.

   ☐ 1 Strongly Disagree   ☐ 2 Disagree   ☐ 3 Undecided   ☐ 4 Agree   ☐ 5 Strongly Agree

4.   I had all the necessary knowledge to perform my specific task.

   ☐ 1 Strongly Disagree   ☐ 2 Disagree   ☐ 3 Undecided   ☐ 4 Agree   ☐ 5 Strongly Agree

5.   Overall, how would you rate your experience with this volunteer opportunity?

   ☐ 1 Excellent   ☐ 2 Good   ☐ 3 Fair   ☐ 4 Poor

Comment: (If you wish, use the space below & on the back to further explain your answers)

PART B

INSTRUCTIONS: Complete Part B if this deployment involved a disaster.

SECTION II. QUESTIONS ABOUT YOUR EXPERIENCES DURING THIS DISASTER DEPLOYMENT: HIGH-RISK FACTORS

During this disaster deployment, did you:

Experience any significant physical injury.

_____Yes   _____No

Feel or express extreme panic.

_____Yes   _____No

Feel that your life was in danger.

_____Yes   _____No

See or hear the death or serious injury of another.

_____Yes   _____No

Experience a confirmed exposure or contamination to a harmful agent.

_____Yes   _____No

Undergo de-contamination

_____Yes   _____No

Receive medical treatment for contamination by a harmful agent.

_____Yes   _____No

SECTION III. QUESTIONS ABOUT YOUR EXPERIENCES SINCE DEPLOYMENT: STRESS SYMPTOMS

Since this disaster deployment, have you:

1. Experienced disturbing memories, thoughts, and/or images related to stressful events experienced during this deployment?

    ☐ 0 Not at all   ☐ 1 Mild; not bothersome   ☐ 2 Moderate; bothersome   ☐ 3 Severe

2. Experienced repeated, disturbing dreams related to stressful events experienced during this deployment?

    ☐ 0 Not at all   ☐ 1 Mild; not bothersome   ☐ 2 Moderate; bothersome   ☐ 3 Severe

3. Felt as if you were reliving a stressful event experienced during this deployment?

    ☐ 0 Not at all   ☐ 1 Mild; not bothersome   ☐ 2 Moderate; bothersome   ☐ 3 Severe

4. Felt very upset when something reminds you of a stressful event experienced during this deployment?

    ☐ 0 Not at all   ☐ 1 Mild; not bothersome   ☐ 2 Moderate; bothersome   ☐ 3 Severe

5. Experienced physical reactions (e.g., heart pounding, trouble breathing, or sweating) when something reminds you of a stressful event experienced during this deployment?

    ☐ 0 Not at all   ☐ 1 Mild; not bothersome   ☐ 2 Moderate; bothersome   ☐ 3 Severe

6. Avoided thinking about or talking about a stressful event experienced during this deployment?

    ☐ 0 Not at all   ☐ 1 Mild; not bothersome   ☐ 2 Moderate; bothersome   ☐ 3 Severe

7. Avoided certain activities or situations because they remind you of a stressful event experience during this deployment?

    ☐ 0 Not at all   ☐ 1 Mild; not bothersome   ☐ 2 Moderate; bothersome   ☐ 3 Severe

8. Had trouble remembering important parts of a stressful event experienced during this deployment?

    ☐ 0 Not at all   ☐ 1 Mild; not bothersome   ☐ 2 Moderate; bothersome   ☐ 3 Severe

9. Experienced a loss of interest in things that you used to enjoy?

☐ 0 Not at all   ☐ 1 Mild; not bothersome   ☐ 2 Moderate; bothersome   ☐ 3 Severe

10.   Felt distant or cut off from other people?

☐ 0 Not at all   ☐ 1 Mild; not bothersome   ☐ 2 Moderate; bothersome   ☐ 3 Severe

11.   Felt emotionally numb?

☐ 0 Not at all   ☐ 1 Mild; not bothersome   ☐ 2 Moderate; bothersome   ☐ 3 Severe

12.   Felt as if your future will somehow be cut short?

☐ 0 Not at all   ☐ 1 Mild; not bothersome   ☐ 2 Moderate; bothersome   ☐ 3 Severe

13.   Had trouble falling or staying asleep?

☐ 0 Not at all   ☐ 1 Mild; not bothersome   ☐ 2 Moderate; bothersome   ☐ 3 Severe

14.   Felt irritable or had angry outbursts?

☐ 0 Not at all   ☐ 1 Mild; not bothersome   ☐ 2 Moderate; bothersome   ☐ 3 Severe

15.   Experienced difficulty concentrating?

☐ 0 Not at all   ☐ 1 Mild; not bothersome   ☐ 2 Moderate; bothersome   ☐ 3 Severe

16.   Been "super alert" or watchful on guard?

☐ 0 Not at all   ☐ 1 Mild; not bothersome   ☐ 2 Moderate; bothersome   ☐ 3 Severe

17.   Felt jumpy or easily startled?

☐ 0 Not at all   ☐ 1 Mild; not bothersome   ☐ 2 Moderate; bothersome   ☐ 3 Severe

It is not unusual to experience some mild symptoms of stress (see your responses to Section III above) after deployment to a disaster. Typically, such symptoms go away on their own. However, if you find yourself experiencing one or more moderate (bothersome) or severe symptoms of stress 3 to 4 weeks after being deployed, you could be experiencing burnout or PTSD.

Continuing stresses described above after an assignment could mean you have thoughts or feelings about your deployment that you have not yet laid to rest. When these continue, they can wear you down and contribute to more severe stress symptoms. Speaking with a mental health professional about your experiences may be all it takes to promote improved coping. Feel free to ask your unit coordinator or the director or coordinator of the Stress Response Team for further information or referral.

In conclusion, expect a readjustment period upon returning home. You may need to make personal reintegration a priority for a while. To help, make every effort to:

- Seek out and give social support.
- Schedule time for a vacation or gradual reintegration into everyday life.
- Prepare for worldview changes that may not be mirrored by others in your life.
- Participate in formal help to address your response to relief work if extreme stress persists for more than two to three weeks.
- Increase leisure activities, stress management, and exercise.
- Pay extra attention to health and nutrition.
- Pay extra attention to rekindling close interpersonal relationships.
- Practice good sleep routines.
- Make time for self-reflection.
- Practice receiving from others.
- Find activities that you enjoy or that make you laugh.
- Try at times not to be in charge or the "expert."
- Increase experiences that have spiritual or philosophical meaning to you.
- Anticipate that you will experience recurring thoughts or dreams and that they will decrease over time.
- Keep a journal to get worries off your mind.
- Ask for help in parenting if you feel irritable or are having difficulties adjusting to being back at home.

Make every effort to avoid:

- Excessive use of alcohol, illicit drugs, or excessive amounts of prescription drugs.
- Making any significant life changes for at least a month.
- Negatively assessing your contribution to relief work.
- Worrying about readjusting.

CHAPTER 15: REBOOT AND PROVIDING CAARE

A principal leadership obligation is taking care of one's team. One term for this notion is "Force Protection." Force Protection refers to the concept of protecting your organization's personnel, equipment, and operations from threats. One of the most significant threats we face revolves around the nature of our work. We work in disasters. Disaster behavioral health assistance team leaders must train their personnel to care for themselves emotionally and physically. This idea might seem paradoxical since our teams comprise health and mental health care professionals, but it is necessary. The author has developed a half-day program that does just that. The program is titled Reboot and Providing CAARE. CAARE stands for Community, Assessment, Alignment, Resilience, and Empathy. These are the program's overarching goals for the individual utilizing the program. The person first assesses their needs and determines which tools to employ to seek alignment, strengthening their resilience, recharging their empathy, and ultimately helping them reconnect with their community. Below is the handout for that program.

Reboot & Providing CAARE

RECHARGING & RESTARTING AFTER DISASTER

INTRODUCTION | PRESENTING CAARE

What is Reboot & Providing CAARE, and why should we discuss it? Since 2020, we have been involved in a pandemic—COVID-19.

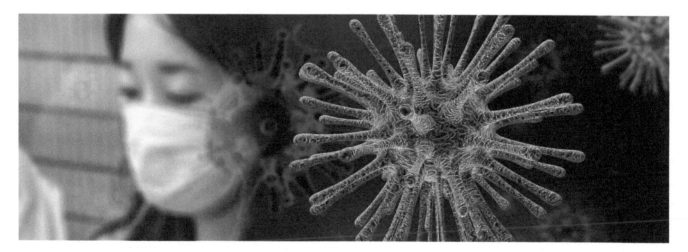

A pandemic is one of the most stressful calamities because it is a prolonged, centripetal disaster with no clear-cut physical or chronological boundaries. The whole world has been and continues to be traumatized. Stress trauma can lead to poor health and even injury. All of us need to work to manage this trauma consciously. CAARE is a specially designed self-help tool developed to achieve this goal.

> "Persistence and resilience only come from having been given the chance to work through difficult problems." ~Gever Tully

What is CAARE?

CAARE is a self-administered process connected to a menu of skills and techniques designed to increase a person's self-efficacy for maintaining emotional and behavioral resilience and connection to family, friends, and community.

CAARE Program Objectives

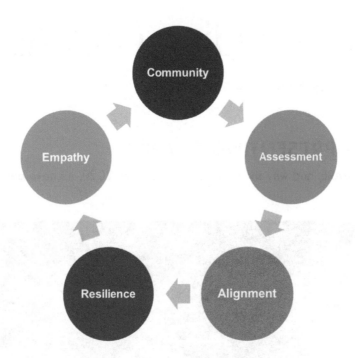

CAARE stands for Community, Assessment, Alignment, Resilience, and Empathy. These are the program's overarching goals for the individual utilizing the program. The person first assesses their needs and determines which tools to employ to seek alignment, strengthening their resilience, recharging their empathy, and ultimately helping them reconnect with their community.

CAARE Program Components

CAARE is comprised of a set of empirically derived skills. There are six Core Actions, each "stand alone." One builds skills with self-monitored tasks. Furthermore, skill-building is achieved via a flexible, tailored approach. Learning and practicing the CAARE skills strengthens one's emotional resilience and empathy, helps prevent mental health problems and maladaptive behaviors, and accelerates recovery from the effects of traumatic stress.

There are six core components of CAARE. These are:

Core Action	Description
Personal Assessment	Obtain necessary information about needs & concerns
Handling Emotions	Minimize arousal & distress
Resolving Problems	Increase self-mastery & enhance the ability to reduce current stresses & problems
Confidence Building	Reduces maladaptive appraisals
Activity Planning	Arrange helpful activities & behaviors
Making Connections	Engage networks, activity levels, prevents withdrawal reactions

CAARE Program Process

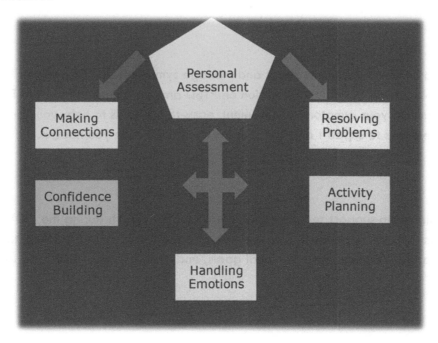

CAARE Program Job Sheets & Smartphone Applications

The CAARE program recommends using job sheets (worksheets) and smartphone applications to aid the individual in utilizing this self-administered and self-monitored process. These latter tools have been selected from those recommended by the Military Health System or the National Center for PTSD and are free to download for both iOS and Android. The following is a list of endorsed applications.

Virtual Hope Box--Contains simple tools to help users with coping, relaxation, distraction, and positive thinking using personalized audio, video, pictures, games, mindfulness exercises, activity planning, inspirational quotes, and coping statements.

Mindfulness Coach--A gradual, self-guided training program designed to help understand and adopt a simple mindfulness practice. It also offers a library of information about mindfulness, 12 audio-guided mindfulness exercises, a mindfulness mastery assessment to help track progress over time, customizable reminders, and access to other support and crisis resources.

The PTSD Coach app can help you learn about and manage symptoms that often occur after trauma. Features include Reliable information on PTSD and treatments that work; Tools for screening and tracking your symptoms; Convenient, easy-to-use tools to help you handle stress symptoms; Direct links to support and help, Always with you when you need it.

COVID Coach—Designed to support self-care and overall mental health during the COVID-19 pandemic. Offers tools for self-care and to improve emotional well-being, trackers to check mood and measure growth toward personal goals, and graphs to visualize progress over time.

PERSONAL ASSESSMENT | CORE ACTION ONE

Personal Assessment aims to gather information to understand our most pressing concerns and then prioritize and plan the appropriate CAARE intervention skill(s). Remember that when deciding what problem to focus on, it is helpful to consider 1) a significant problem, 2) one that is causing severe distress, 3) a problem that needs to be addressed sooner than others, 4) a problem that is worsening over time, and 5) addressing that problem will reduce others. Use the CAARE Screening Form job sheets and the CAARE Skills Selection Chart to make an Action Plan.

CAARE SCREENING FORM

Problem Area	Describe the Problem
Physical Health Am I worried about my physical health? *Yes or No*	
Emotional Health Am I worried about my emotional health? *Yes or No*	
Interpersonal Functioning Do I have concerns about how I am getting along with others? *Yes or No*	
Substance Use/Abuse Am I concerned that I may be abusing substances, alcohol, or prescription medication? *Yes or No*	
Basic Requirements Am I worried about meeting the basic requirements of everyday life? *Yes or No*	
Other Worries Am I worried about something else not mentioned about? *Yes or No*	

CAARE SKILLS SELECTION CHART

Problem Area	Primary CAARE Core Action Skill
I have a tough problem I need to solve.	Resolving Problems Confidence Building
I am having intense and upsetting emotional reactions.	Handling Emotions Making Connections Confidence Building
I am feeling depressed, sad, and alone.	Handling Emotions Activity Planning Making Connections
I am having negative thoughts that are overwhelming any positive thinking.	Confidence Building Activity Planning
I don't know how to connect to people any more. I don't have enough people I can count on.	Making Connections Activity Planning Confidence Building
I am experiencing a serious physical, emotional, or substance abuse problem and need help.	Resolving Problems Confidence Building Making Connections

Personal Assessment Smartphone Applications to Consider

The following applications contain tools that can help with Personal Assessment.

VA's **Live Whole Health** app is a free, easy-to-use tool created for Veterans and others ready to take the next step in their Whole Health journey. Whole Health is VA's holistic approach to care that supports your health and well-being. Whole Health centers care about what matters to you, not what is the matter with you. This app lets you fill out your health inventory, set goals, and learn about Whole Health.

HANDLING EMOTIONS | CORE ACTION TWO

Distressing emotions can negatively affect mood, decision-making, interpersonal relationships, daily functioning, and health. Learning skills to manage these reactions can protect our health, improve self-confidence, enhance interpersonal relationships, and reduce maladaptive efforts at coping.

The Action Steps of Handling Emotions are 1) identifying distressing reactions and their triggers, 2) learning skills to address priority reactions, and 3) creating a plan to manage the identified reaction.

Skill Category	Description
Calming Skills	Breathing retraining, self-talk, meditation, etc.
Skills to Put Thoughts & Feelings into Words	Writing exercises
Skills to Recognize & Manage Triggers	Identifying reminders and ways to cope with them before, during, and after the trigger
Skills to Develop a Personalized Strategy	To manage reactions like anger, grief, sleep difficulties, worries

To make an Action Plan, use the following job sheet.

HANDLING EMOTIONS JOBSHEET

1. Describe the upsetting emotion and the situation.
   Rank: 1 (Not very distressing) - 2 - 3 - 4 - 5 (Very distressing)

2. Check the skills you could use to feel better.

   ___Calming skills: breathing retraining, self-talk, meditation
   ___Skills to put thoughts & feelings into words: writing exercises
   ___Skills to recognize & manage triggers: identifying reminders and
      ways to cope with them before, during, and after the trigger.
   ___Skills to develop a personalized strategy: to manage reactions like
      anger, grief, sleep difficulties, worries.

3. Make a plan—address each upsetting emotion and situation, address
   what to do before, during, & after the upsetting situation.

Handling Emotions Smartphone Applications to Consider

The following applications contain tools that can help with Handling Emotions.

How We Feel is a free app created by scientists, designers, engineers, and therapists to help people better understand their emotions and find strategies to help them navigate their feelings in the moment. Conceived in conjunction with Yale University's Center for Emotional Intelligence and based on the work of Dr. Marc Brackett, How We Feel helps people find the right word to describe how they feel while tracking their sleep, exercise, and health trends using HealthKit to spot patterns over time.

RESOLVING PROBLEMS | CORE ACTION THREE

Continuing problems and ongoing adversities can add to our stress levels, distract us from self-care, and help us maintain traumatic stress reactions. There are four steps to Resolving Problems: 1) define the problem & decide ownership, 2) set the goal, 3) brainstorm, and 4) evaluate and choose the best option.

When defining the problem, ask 1) how often it happens, 2) who is involved, 3) how does it make me feel, and 4) how does it impact me? When deciding ownership, ask 1) is this problem something happening between me and someone else or 2) is this problem mainly happening to someone else or between other people? If your answer is #2, it is a problem you cannot resolve. When brainstorming, identify different solutions and write them down. After the list is generated, identify potential consequences for each solution. Remember that the concept of "solution" is more likely finding ways to improve the situation in small ways that count rather than totally solving the problem.

To make an Action Plan, use the following Job Sheet.

RESOLVING PROBLEMS JOBSHEET

1. **What problem do I want to resolve?**

2. **What is my goal—what do I want to happen?**

3. **What are some resolution options (brainstorm 5 to 10)?**

4. **What action (#3 above) might be my best resolution option & how do I implement it?**

Resolving Problems Smartphone Applications to Consider
The following applications contain tools that can help with Resolving Problems.

 The **PTSD Coach** app can help you learn about and manage symptoms that often occur after trauma. Features include Reliable information on PTSD and treatments that work; Tools for screening and tracking your symptoms; Convenient, easy-to-use tools to help you handle stress symptoms; Direct links to support and help, Always with you when you need it.

Tools include guided relaxation exercises, soothing sounds and images, relationship tips, and more. You can customize these tools and integrate your contacts, music, and photos.

CONFIDENCE BUILDING | CORE ACTION FOUR

Thoughts about self and events shape how we feel and act. Distressing thoughts can maintain negative emotions. However, we can change the focus of our thoughts to those that make us feel hopeful and less overwhelmed. Focusing on useful thoughts improves mood and paves the way for resilience. The goal of Confidence Building is to look at how our negative thoughts affect our feelings and behavior and then to identify and practice healthy ways of thinking. Remember, thought is unhelpful if it makes it more challenging to deal with the situation by increasing feelings of being overwhelmed or hopeless.

CONFIDENCE BUILDING JOBSHEET

1. Identify unhelpful thoughts (& associated feeling) & under what circumstances they occur.
   a. Thoughts

   b. Feelings

2. Identify useful thoughts (& associated feelings) that could replace those in #1.
   a. New Thoughts

   b. New Feelings

3. Schedule practice of the useful thoughts. For example, imagine the circumstance where you experience the unhelpful thought and feeling, but this time practice saying the useful thought out loud while imagining yourself feeling the new, associated emotion. Remember the Confidence Building Equation.

Resolving Problems Smartphone Applications to Consider

The following applications contain tools that can help with Confidence Building.

The **PTSD Coach** app can help you learn about and manage symptoms that often occur after trauma. Features include Reliable information on PTSD and treatments that work; Tools for screening and tracking your symptoms; Convenient, easy-to-use tools to help you handle stress symptoms; Direct links to support and help; Always with you when you need it.

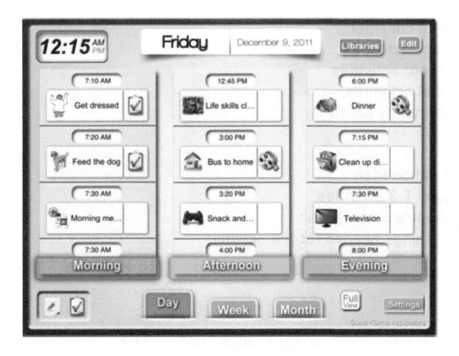

People become depressed, down, and apathetic when they no longer engage in pleasurable activities. The goals of Activity Planning are 1) to restore a sense of control and normalcy; 2) to help overcome feelings of sadness, hopelessness, fearfulness, or general lack of energy; and 3) to reconnect with others. Activity Planning steps include 1) identifying and planning one or more activities and 2) scheduling these activities in a calendar. Select activities that are enjoyable, achievable, and practical.

To make an Action Plan, use the following job sheet.

ACTIVITY PLANNING JOBSHEET

1. Activities to consider
   a. Indoor activities
   b. Outdoor activities
   c. Social activities
   d. Community activities

2. Make an Action Plan
   a. Select 1-3 activities
   b. Schedule on calendar
   c. List things needed for the activity

Activity Planning Smartphone Applications to Consider

The following application can help with Activity Planning.

Positive Activity Jackpot--Helps users who may be overwhelmed by depression find nearby enjoyable activities. Can't decide? Let the app's jackpot function make the choice. See "Resources" for a clinician's guide.

MAKING CONNECTIONS | CORE ACTION SIX

Positive social support has been consistently identified as a critical protective factor in studies of disaster survivors. Conversely, a lack of social support has been identified as predicting poor outcomes. Making Connections aims to increase connections to positive relationships and community support. The steps of Making Connections are 1) develop a Community Connections Diagram, 2) review the Community Connections Diagram, and 3) make and follow a Community Care Blueprint.

When creating a Community Connections Diagram, use paper and pen to map or draw out your most important social connections/relationships. Only put in people who are readily accessible at the moment. Start with people in your community and then add people you mainly communicate with by phone, text, or email. Put in individuals and groups, no more than ten.

COMMUNITY CONNECTIONS DIAGRAM

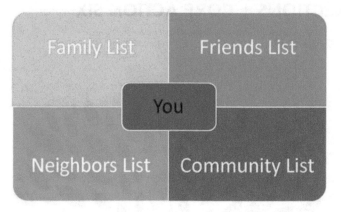

CONCLUSION | TIME FOR YOU TO TAKE CHARGE

After identifying areas in need of improvement, make a Community Care Blueprint. Identify one place to change and make an Action Plan.

Community Care Blueprint	
Identify an area to change to increase connections.	
What do I want to happen?	
Whom should I ask for support to connect with?	
When is the right time? Right place?	
Develop an "I message" to request support.	
Make a 'thank you' statement.	

It's time for you to take charge. Use the information you've learned in this course and presented in this booklet and begin.

> Courage doesn't always roar. Sometimes courage is the quiet voice at the end of the day saying, 'I will try again tomorrow.'
>
> ~Mary Anne Radmacher

Made in the USA
Monee, IL
18 September 2024

66137679R00077